Aging Matters Press
2021

I hear you.

Talking and listening to people with Alzheimer's

JANE L. MAHAKIAN, PhD and ALYSON KUHN

To all of my patients, who have enriched my life and taught me to be present in the moment.

— J.L.M.

To my sister Nancy, without whose boundless encouragement and humor, I couldn't have and wouldn't have.

— A.K.

Thus, the impact of biological changes on our lives at all ages can be made worse—or better—by our environment.

— Louise Aronson, MD
Elderhood

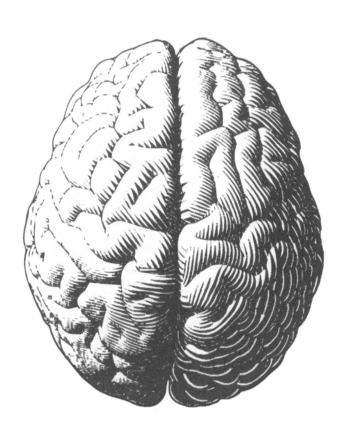

I hear you.

Talking and listening to people with Alzheimer's
(and other dementias)

Foreword

William Rodman Shankle, MS MD FACP

FROM A SCIENTIFIC PERSPECTIVE, the final frontier is not *space*, as Star Trek proclaimed, but rather the *understanding of behavior*. We are a long way from such understanding. There are few resources that provide such a clear understanding of what drives behavioral problems in each individual with a dementing disorder. Dr. Jane Mahakian's direct experience, knowledge, and wisdom in finding solutions to these difficult problems is akin to that of an artist applying their creativity to express a new way of seeing the world.

Since 1988, for the past 32 years, I have solely devoted my career as a physician to diagnosing, treating, managing, researching and understanding dementing disorders due to Alzheimer's disease and other causes of brain degeneration. Much has changed. We have entered the era of preventing, partly reversing, halting or greatly delaying the progression of dementing disorders.

What has not changed is that the management of behavioral problems directly related to these dementing disorders remains the greatest challenge, frustration and hardship to patients, their loved ones, and the healthcare professionals who care for them. *Desperation* is probably the single word that best captures the emotional state of patients, their loved ones, and those who try to treat behavioral problems when they arise.

Through the expressive writing of Alyson Kuhn, Dr. Jane Mahakian describes the bewildering, and sometimes terrifying, behaviors of individuals that she and I have been asked to understand, treat and manage. From her three decades of experience working with patients and their families with dementing disorders, Dr. Mahakian shows us, through well selected and engaging individual stories, that *there are human solutions to human problems.*

The solutions are usually found in a detailed understanding of the individual and their surroundings. Explicitly, behavioral problems arise from a complex interaction of an individual's personality and traumatic life experiences, their dementing disorder and its severity, their coexisting medical conditions and degree of control, their medications, their daily routine and engagement with others, and recent events such as falls, head and body injuries, colds, flus, operations, procedures, travels, displacement from their usual environment, loss of a loved one, et cetera. To effectively understand and manage behavioral problems, "the devil is in the details."

Enjoy and learn from this work of love.

W. R. Shankle, MS MD FACP
January, 2021

Introduction

Dr. Jane L. Mahakian

WHEN I SET OUT TO WRITE THIS BOOK with co-author Alyson Kuhn, we were challenged to decide how to refer to someone living with dementia. Some writers use "your loved one" or "your family member," but neither of these seemed adequate to us, as the person may not be part of your family. He or she may be someone you work with (a client, a patient, a colleague), a close friend, or someone you know more casually. Whereas cancer patients can be described as "cancer patients," and someone with bipolar disorder can be described as "bipolar," we did not want to describe people living with dementia as "demented." So, we have named our prototypical person living with dementia, Robin. Robin may be a man or a woman, but we always refer to Robin as *she.*

This book's intention is to help the growing number of us who want to be able to talk and listen comfortably to people with dementia. Many of us feel that dementia is lurking behind a half-open door. It can be tempting to close the door, by ignoring your intuition or disregarding symptoms. But this can isolate Robin and even put her in harm's way. *I hear you* will show you how to open the door, to join Robin in the realm of dementia, and to communicate with her in the best way for both of you.

I refer to anyone with dementia to whom I consult as my patient, regardless of whether she lives in her own home or in a care community. Consulting with someone may involve seeing her only once, for a scheduled assessment or evaluation, or in response to an emergency. Conversely, I may manage her care on an ongoing basis for months or years. Some families and primary care physicians rely on me for guidance and problem solving.

Frequently, I am asked to make recommendations about next steps, including moving a patient from her home to a care community. This process often involves providing transitional counseling to both my patient and her family. Over the years, I have told countless clients—family members as well as fiduciaries and conservators— that Robin can still have and deserves a high quality of life. I typically make recommendations for improving Robin's well-being as her disease progresses.

Talking and listening are key to nurturing Robin and to enjoying your times together. Although each person's dementia trajectory is unique, there are certain signposts that many have in common, and I have seen most of them numerous times. So, I can loan you my compass, the same one I have used for 30-plus years to navigate the realm of dementia. And I can promise that you have the ability to learn how to create and share rich moments with Robin along the way.

One of my priorities is to provide people with dementia the opportunity to experience meaningful connections and a full range of emotions, including feeling useful. You can enrich Robin's moment-living life, and this is a gift to her. Some of us without dementia may tend to discount the worth of people with dementia, to feel that they are diminished, no longer complete, and even no longer very useful. But people with dementia do still have feelings, and their ability to feel does not fade. Similarly, their desire to be useful or helpful does not fade. In this way, they are like everyone else in the world. Your goal, your opportunity, is to make Robin feel like there is nothing wrong with her. This is a big part of what this book is about.

MY EPIPHANY

In 1987, I was at the beginning of my graduate studies. Little did I know that sharing a girls' weekend in Las Vegas that spring with my 83-year-old grandmother Rose would shape the direction of my life's work.

Grandma had forgetfulness, but still loved to play the slot machines. She also loved to win. On Saturday mid-morning, Grandma was happily playing a dollar slot machine, with just a few dollars left in her wallet. She proposed "Let's go eat lunch, then get more money out of the ATM, and when we come back, I will play this machine again."

Fast forward two hours, we returned to the casino. Grandma stopped and declared, "Aha, here is MY machine." In fact, this was not her machine. After going back and forth with "No, Grandma, this is not your machine—it's the one in the next row," I realized I had lost. She began to play, happily dropping dollar after dollar into the machine.

Fifteen minutes later, she hit the jackpot of $2,500! Triumphant, with a big grin, she turned to me and said, "You know, honey, I know you are studying to become a doctor and work with old people, but I want you to remember one thing—we are always right!" And she was right. I also hit the jackpot that day, because that bit of grandmotherly wisdom has formed the basis of my philosophy as a gerontologist.

MY DEMENTIA-CENTERED APPROACH

The dementia-centered approach I have developed is realistic, practical, and effective. I meet my patients where they are, physically as well as figuratively. By this I mean that my conversations are always based on where someone is in terms of cognitive functioning. I have a sense of where the person usually "is," but this can change from moment to moment. Obviously, I can't simply ask, "Where are you now?" but I can be observant and start a conversation in a way that the person with dementia will actually direct—and then I respond in kind. You can learn to do this, even though it may seem counterintuitive at first.

My goal is to care for the complete person, so I factor in a patient's psychological, social, and spiritual situation as well as his or her physical and mental needs and limitations. I focus on the person rather than on his or her dementia, which cannot be treated per se. But the dementia is at the center, and it would be counterproductive to tiptoe around it. By focusing on Robin and what she can do, not on what she cannot, I am entering her world, rather than expecting her to jump back into ours. My work is largely about making people with dementia feel good about themselves, as though there is nothing wrong with them.

One of my favorite testimonials came in an email from a man named George, who I'd only met with for a single one-hour consultation. He was frustrated by how challenging it had become to visit his wife Rita at her memory care community. We talked about Rita, and I made some suggestions. A week later, George emailed me to report: "I tried changing the way I talk with Rita. I have found that if I take my agenda and let it go and strictly pay attention to where she is, our time together is much enriched and far more satisfying! And, I do not feel stressed from the experience and truly come away feeling closer to her. I'm surprised and so grateful to you!"

Reflections of a Dementia Daughter: Why I wanted to write this book

Alyson Kuhn

THE SHORT EXPLANATION IS that as a daughter, and holder of my mother's medical power of attorney, there was no book—to the best of my knowledge—like this, and there desperately needed to be. As a writer, I realized that publishing a book with Dr. Jane Mahakian could help a lot of people feel more comfortable talking and listening—to actually remain connected—to those with dementia. My deep wish is that *I hear you* will indirectly also help people with dementia, by increasing the attention and kindness they receive from the rest of us.

The longer, more personal explanation starts here: When I realized that the time had come to move my mother, Caroline, from her home to a care community, I was overwhelmed, both logistically and emotionally. I thought there was a huge likelihood that she would come to hate me, to blame me for taking away the future she had envisioned for herself after her retirement. And that was a risk I felt I had to take. Fortunately, incredibly, that didn't happen, and I think that this was largely thanks to my ability to entice rather than to confront or contradict—and to tell my mother untruths when the truth would have been frightening or hurtful. My therapeutic fibs, as they are commonly called, did more than increase Caroline's sense of well-being, they made her feel loved. (Dr. Jane and I refer to these as "the *kind* kind of lie.") My close relationship with my mother deepened as her dementia progressed, and we shared many, many moments of candor, delight, and joy.

My mother moved from her home in 2003. I was in my early 50s then, I am in my late 60s now, and my interest in how our society can take better care of people with dementia has intensified. My two siblings, Bruce and Nancy, and I had several major advantages in figuring out the best way to care for our mother. And even with these advantages, the next nine years sometimes felt like a roller coaster. Dr. Jane helped orchestrate Caroline's move from her home and continued to visit her and consult with our family for several years. Our family friend Gladys Abney (a.k.a. Gladiola) became Caroline's main companion. Gladys made every appointment into a little adventure, and she could charm Caroline into doing almost anything. They laughed a lot. Gladys was also physically stronger than I, and savvier about how to help Caroline into and out of a vehicle. And, last but not least, Caroline had the financial resources to live in a memory care community in San Francisco. Without these advantages, perhaps I would have tried to put dementia out of my mind after my mother's death, rather than writing this book to honor my memory of her.

Learning to communicate with someone with dementia is an enormous first step toward making that person's life easier and richer in the moment. The more of us who want to talk and listen to people with dementia, the less "socially disappeared" these people will be. The stigma surrounding dementia seems to be starting to lift, and co-authoring this book is my effort to increase awareness, compassion, and hope. In these pages, you will find myriad insights, simple explanations, real-life stories, and much practical wisdom distilled from Dr. Jane's 30-plus years of experience and advocacy in the realm of forgetfulness. I believe, from the bottom of my heart, that entering the moment-by-moment-living reality of someone with dementia is not only worthwhile for their sake, but also rewarding for you.

Ways to Use This Book

YOU CAN TELL BY THE SIZE of *I hear you* that it does not aim to be encyclopedic. Its goal is to be helpful, so it needs to be enticing to read. It is practical rather than academic, with all the citation footnotes located at the back. The table of contents is very detailed, to make it easier to find and revisit topics of particular interest to you. The book has no index, because it would have listed dozens and dozens of entries for "behaviors," "dementia," "empowering," "purpose," and so forth—which would not be very helpful.

Each of the seven chapters includes one or two vignettes, for a total of eleven. Four of them are personal accounts by co-author Alyson Kuhn of experiences with her mother, Caroline, who lived gracefully with dementia for over ten years. The particulars of these events are as Alyson remembers them, acknowledging that her own memory is not perfect. The families portrayed in the other seven vignettes are composites, based on Dr. Jane's decades of clinical experience as a gerontologist. Though the characters in the composite vignettes are fictitious except for Dr. Jane herself, the situations and solutions described are all true-to-life examples.

You might decide to start by reading a vignette or two or three. You may find yourself nodding or smiling in recognition and agreement, or you may be touched or surprised. The vignettes are intended to help you "listen in on" and then consider a scenario that is in some ways applicable to how you talk and listen to someone you know with dementia. If reading the vignettes encourages you to write down your own observations and feelings in story form, so much the better!

I hear you is not strictly chronological in terms of the progression of Alzheimer's or other dementias, so you do not need to read the chapters in order. All of them include key principles for talking and listening to people with dementia, so each chapter is fairly self-contained.

This book will be helpful not only to family members and professional caregivers, but also to friends and colleagues who are apprehensive about spending time with someone with Alzheimer's. You can pick up *I hear you* at the end of a long day, open it almost anywhere, read a page or two, and go to sleep feeling a bit more confident about the prospect of talking and listening to someone you care about who is living with dementia.

1

Clarifying Three of the Four D-words: Dementia, Depression & Diagnosis

THIS BOOK'S MAIN GOAL is to help you *care for*—meaning *to take care of*—and continue to *care about* Robin* as a person. Many people let the caregiving part overshadow the emotional connection. Truly communicating with Robin is key to her well-being, and yet this aspect of interacting with her makes many of us nervous or on edge. Dementia in general and Alzheimer's disease in particular have nasty reputations.

For a multitude of reasons, the symptoms of dementia seem more mysterious, more random, and scarier than those of purely physical ailments. Their impact on family and friends tends to be more challenging than that of other diseases. And many of us have "Alzheimer's anxiety" for ourselves as well as for our loved ones.

Dementia is a disease whose root cause we cannot see, because it is inside the brain. It is helpful to get clear on what dementia is and how it progresses. A good starting point is to understand what dementia is not. It is not a mental illness, psychiatric problem, or behavioral disorder. And, last but not least, it is not necessarily an illness of old age. Scientists are still not sure what causes dementia, though researchers continue to make significant discoveries. As yet, there is no cure, nor a guaranteed way to prevent the disease or even to permanently slow its progress.

---

*Robin is our prototypical person living with dementia. Robin may be a man or a woman, though we always refer to Robin as *she*.

Let's consider: that dementia is a disease it is tempting to ignore or deny. Sadly, fear, stigma, and the expense of care cause many families to delay diagnosis and treatment.

Dementia itself is not physically painful, meaning that it does not usually make Robin's head hurt. Most people with dementia are unaware of their diagnosis. But, even if Robin does not realize exactly what is going on, the effects of her dementia are probably emotionally painful for her. And her dementia is probably emotionally painful for you, because you cannot discuss it with her. Dementia is different from managing a physical ailment where you and Robin might talk about her symptoms, the course of treatment, the prognosis, and how she is feeling. Because Robin may not be aware of the limitations imposed by her dementia, she is not going to thank you for helping her compensate for them. Although she may thank you for your various kindnesses, she will not link them to her dementia.

Learning to communicate with Robin in *her* world is essential. Robin's dementia is not a separate item on the daunting checklist of things someone will now have to figure out: paperwork, nutrition, medical appointments, errands, finances, and so on. Her dementia needs to be at the center of "Team Robin's" plan, and of every interaction. Robin's dementia explains and excuses what she says, sometimes repeatedly; what she does; and what she needs. Her progressive cognitive impairments may make you feel that the old Robin is fading away. But she is still there.

You may feel unsure how to respond to Robin, especially when she says something that you consider untrue or wrong, something that does not reflect *your* reality. So, dementia is a disruptor, not only of Robin's day-to-day life, her independence and her future, but also of your relationship with her. You may feel deprived or cheated of the essence of the person you knew. And this may make you uncomfortable or sad or even angry—for reasons that Robin probably cannot fathom. Your feelings are understandable, but they are not particularly productive. Robin has not *chosen* to become forgetful, and you cannot fix her forgetfulness. You may find yourself anxious and frustrated if you cannot "go where Robin is." Robin in turn may become anxious and confused if you persist in telling her things that do not make sense to her.

COMMON QUESTIONS ABOUT DEMENTIA

The causes of dementia are multifactorial, and understanding a few basics about the various types of dementia may help you think differently about interacting with Robin. Dr. Jane has worked in the realm of forgetfulness for more than thirty years. She finds— despite the profusion of research findings, popular books, videos, and media attention—that many people trying to care for a loved one with dementia are still confused about the disease and how to communicate with someone who has it. Frequently, part of people's squeamishness with dementia stems from a lack of accurate information. Misinformation proliferates because dementia has become big business.

The questions Dr. Jane is asked most frequently—in family consultations, caregiver support groups, and training sessions— range from the most basic to the most personal.

The 10 questions

① What is dementia?

② Are there different types of dementia?

③ Is Alzheimer's disease different from dementia?

④ Can Alzheimer's be stopped or reversed?

⑤ Do more women than men get dementia?

⑥ How can you tell if someone has dementia?

⑦ Does someone who has dementia realize it?

⑧ Have scientists discovered how to prevent getting dementia?

⑨ How long do most people live with dementia?

⑩ Will my mother (or father or spouse or sibling or best friend) still know who I am?

1   What is dementia?

Dementia is an umbrella term for a collection of symptoms, rather than a specific disease. It is not a normal part of aging. Dementia is characterized by a decline in cognitive ability severe enough to interfere with day-to-day living. The most commonly occurring symptoms are: short-term memory loss, diminishing ability to think and remember, emotional problems, difficulties with language, decreased motivation, and a state of confusion.

Just because someone—including yourself, perhaps—has one or more of these symptoms, does not mean he or she has dementia. The key question is, *What is causing these symptoms?* It may be as simple as being overtired, having too much on your plate, feeling stressed or under the weather. Even a urinary tract infection can result in symptoms like these. Medication imbalances can also cause temporary confusion, depression, low energy, and memory lapses. Ditto dehydration.

2   Are there different types of dementia?

Yes, emphatically yes. Alzheimer's disease is the most common, and the most talked about, type of dementia. Researchers have identified many different causes of dementia—some studies enumerate dozens. The various causes affect people differently. In other words: everyone's dementia is somewhat distinctive, which really is not so surprising, as each of us has a brain that is uniquely ours. Starting on p. 8, you'll find an overview of the three main classifications of memory impairment and their most prevalent causes and symptoms.

3   Is Alzheimer's disease different from dementia?

Alzheimer's disease is the most common form of dementia. About 60–80 percent of all diagnosed dementias are of the Alzheimer's type.[1] Accepted estimates are that the chances of developing Alzheimer's double every five years from age 65 to 85.[2]

Can Alzheimer's be stopped or reversed?

Most physicians, researchers, and other specialists agree that this type of dementia is irreversible.[3] Scientists have some hope of slowing the progression, but study results to date are still inconclusive.[4]

Do more women than men get dementia?

Yes. It is widely reported that women account for nearly two-thirds of people with Alzheimer's disease.[5] Women tend to live longer than men, and the chances of developing Alzheimer's increase with age, but this alone does not explain the prevalence of Alzheimer's in women. Sixteen percent of women in their 70s and above have Alzheimer's or some other dementia, compared with 11 percent of men.[6]

How can you tell if someone has dementia?

Short-term memory loss is the hallmark symptom of dementia. It is the most common symptom, and it is frequently the earliest indicator to show up. As mentioned earlier, just because someone has one or more of the following symptoms, does not necessarily mean he or she has dementia.

Starting on p.10, you will find a detailed description of common symptoms of Alzheimer's-type dementia. The list is simple to follow, and puts a name with symptoms that you may not have had an easy way to describe.

7

Does someone who has dementia realize it?

Sometimes yes, and sometimes no. Some people with dementia are aware of their cognitive challenges, while others are not. Everyone's reality is their own. The lack of insight and awareness of cognitive impairment is a neurological condition called anosognosia (from the Ancient Greek: without + disease + knowledge). This is different than denial.

8

Have scientists discovered how to prevent getting dementia?

The short answer is *not yet*. The general medical recommendations for a healthy, active lifestyle are considered the best preventive ways to forestall dementia.[7,8] Current research supports the idea that, although dementia is not contagious, some people may have a genetic predisposition to Alzheimer's in particular. Recently, several large studies have confirmed that healthy eating seems to be helpful—a Mediterranean diet in particular. Supplements and specific "miracle" foods tend to go in and out of fashion, so buyer beware. Exercise is also being touted as a good way to stave off dementia. Doctors support the value of social connection, whether with people in your neighborhood or community, at a day program, or in an assisted living situation.

9

How long do most people live with dementia?

With Alzheimer's disease, life expectancy varies considerably. Often, people are not diagnosed until several years after the onset of dementia symptoms, which makes their post-diagnosis life expectancy shorter. Very generally speaking, the average life expectancy after onset is 7 to 10 years. Sometimes, however, Alzheimer's progresses quickly, and life expectancy can be as short as three years.[9]

10

Will my mother (or father or spouse or sibling or best friend) still know who I am?

Those of us without dementia are so invested in our identities that we find this aspect of dementia particularly frightening. My personal belief, based on caring for hundreds of patients, is that your loved one continues to know who you are even as the dementia progresses. Sometimes, as part of someone's momentary confusion, she may mistake you for your sibling or your parent, but that confusion is not constant or permanent. It is disconcerting, and you cannot correct the person, but do not take it personally. I believe that as dementia progresses and the person's verbal abilities decline, she may stop addressing you by name, but that does not mean she does not recognize you or is not glad to see you.

Basic overview: the three main types of memory impairment

Mild cognitive impairment (MCI) usually manifests in middle age; it is not reversible, but neither is it necessarily a precursor to developing an Alzheimer's-type dementia. MCI is characterized by deficits in memory that do not significantly impact the person's daily functioning. Some people's MCI is stable for decades, or even for the rest of their lives. They may continue to work and to function at a high level for a period of years.

Conversely, if someone's MCI worsens, they may begin to forget upcoming appointments and social engagements more frequently. They may lose their train of thought more easily, including having trouble following conversations (or the storyline in a book or movie). They may become overwhelmed at having to make decisions. They may become more impulsive and exhibit poor judgment, such as tipping the waiter $100.00.

Reversible dementia can mimic the behaviors of irreversible dementia, in terms of cognitive or behavioral symptoms. Reversible dementia is typically caused by a temporary medical condition that can be corrected, such as a urinary tract or other infection, depression (See **depression**, p.11), medication mismanagement, delirium (See **delirium**, p.12), or certain head injuries. Some medication imbalances or nutritional deficiencies (including vitamins) can provoke symptoms that resemble those of dementia.

> **Dehydration** is notorious for causing increased confusion and lethargy. Many older people limit their intake of water to avoid needing to use the toilet, especially during the night.

> **Polypharmacy**, which refers to taking multiple medications, is another risk factor. Various drugs' interactions, combined dosages, and cumulative effects may mimic dementia and/or depression. It is critical that all prescribing doctors be aware of all medications a patient takes, including supplements.

> **Hearing loss** can cause confusion and depression and can accelerate the onset of cognitive impairment. Many people are actually unaware of their hearing loss, and it's vital to get Robin's hearing checked. Recent studies confirm that older people with even mild hearing loss are likelier to develop dementia than those whose hearing is still "youthful." Moderate and severe hearing loss are progressively even more of a risk predictor. There is not necessarily any causality between hearing loss and dementia, but getting a hearing test is relatively simple and may have significant short- and longer-term benefits.[10]

Irreversible dementia is a progressive, degenerative disease that gradually reduces a person's ability to function in everyday life. Alzheimer's disease is the most common type of irreversible dementia, affecting approximately 80 percent of people diagnosed with dementia. Alzheimer's compromises not only short-term memory (the hallmark symptom), but also impairs the parts of the brain responsible for problem solving and judgment.

Another form of irreversible dementia is **frontotemporal dementia (FTD)**. This neurodegenerative disorder is named for the lobes of the brain it adversely affects. It is far more prevalent in men (70 percent) than in women.[11] Many patients with FTD (40 percent) have a family history of dementia.[12] FTD is the second most common early-onset form of dementia, usually showing up between the ages of 45 and 65.[13] People suffering from FTD are often erratic or impulsive in social situations, typically not caring about their behavior.[14] As FTD progresses, many patients exhibit increasingly problematic, and even violent, behaviors. This makes it difficult, and potentially risky, to care for them at home. For some patients, behavioral counseling, a structured environment, and medications can be effective in calming these behaviors. Diagnosing can be tricky, as FTD often masks other illnesses. Some neurologists specialize in treating patients with FTD.

Common symptoms of Alzheimer's-type dementia

Short-term memory loss is the hallmark symptom of dementia. It is both the most common symptom and frequently the earliest to show up. Repetition and confusion are part and parcel of this. Wandering off and getting lost, frequently dramatized on television and in the movies, is a major safety concern in the middle-to-late stages of dementia.

Repetition is one of the most apparent (and irritating for you) results of short-term memory loss. In addition to asking the same question over and over, Robin may also tell the same story over and over in a matter of minutes (and take offense if the repetition is remarked upon).

Confusion may be less apparent than repetition, so it's all the more important to watch out for. To make matters murkier, Robin may sense her confusion and try to cover it up. The situation isn't black-and-white; you need to be on the lookout for shades of gray.

Executive functioning refers to the high-level ability to plan and organize thoughts and activities, and to control emotions. Permanent damage to the brain's frontal lobes leads not only to diminished reasoning capabilities but also to a decreased ability to regulate emotional behavior.

Language and speech may become "casualties" of advancing dementia. One common sign of deteriorating verbal ability is not being able to find the right word. For example, Robin has recently started referring to her pen as "that thing I write with." As it becomes more difficult for her to express a complex thought, she may start a sentence and then simply stop midway through. She instantly forgets what she was going to say, or even what the topic was.

Personality, behavior, and social skills may shift gradually. Most people with dementia retain their personality for a period of time. In fact, in certain instances, someone's personality may initially be heightened or intensified with the onset of dementia. Robin may retain her social graces long after her cognitive skills decline.

DEPRESSION & DEMENTIA: A DECEPTIVE DUO

Depression frequently accompanies dementia. Doctors are not of one mind about the relationship between dementia and depression. There is some evidence to suggest that (1) an acute depression can predispose someone to develop dementia, and (2) the biological changes caused by Alzheimer's may intensify a predisposition to depression. Current estimates are that between 30 and 40 percent of people being treated for dementia have an accompanying depression. In some people, a depression may become so incapacitating that it actually mimics dementia. Conversely, dementia is sometimes misdiagnosed as depression. A neurologist has the expertise to discern which of Robin's symptoms are attributable to dementia, depression, or other medical problems, and then to develop an appropriate care plan.

Delirium is an acute, temporary state, usually caused by an illness or by medication, including anesthesia. It can last as long as a week, and then it may take several weeks for Robin to rebound to her previous level of functioning. In other instances, the delirium can be of very short duration, and may be resolved, often by medication, with no apparent after effects.

Someone with MCI may well become depressed, whether or not she is aware of the changes that family and friends notice. She may be afraid to say anything, and may try to hide or disguise her confusion or anxiety. The stress of this may lead to irritability or depression. She may seem apathetic about the future or about things she has enjoyed in the past. She may feel as if she is straddling an uncomfortable fence—particularly if friends and family make jokes about their own senior moments. This sort of depression is not necessarily an indication of advancing dementia. A neurologist will be able to determine what is behind the depression and whether antidepressant or other medications might mitigate the problem.

THE VALUE OF AN ACCURATE DIAGNOSIS

An early, accurate diagnosis can be extremely helpful in terms of formulating a care plan for Robin. An additional benefit to seeking a diagnosis earlier than later is that Robin may be able to understand why she is experiencing these symptoms and what can be done in terms of early treatment to slow the progression. Hearing these things from a neurologist is usually somewhat less distressing, less personal, than hearing them from family.

Some healthcare professionals think all patients with dementia should be informed of their diagnosis, while others are not of the same opinion. One size of candor does not fit all patients. An 80-year-old person diagnosed with mid-stage Alzheimer's may not have much to gain by being made aware of her diagnosis. She could become terrified by the idea that she has Alzheimer's. Conversely, a younger person may want to know her diagnosis, so that she has a better understanding of her treatment options and can plan accordingly. (In Chapter 2, *Acknowledging Early-Onset Dementia*, you can read about the importance of having a neurologist on your team who treats each patient proactively.)

Until relatively recently, doctors were only definitively able to confirm a diagnosis of Alzheimer's by performing an autopsy to detect the presence of plaque (also referred to as brain tangles). Now, however, scientists are working on ways to confirm a diagnosis of Alzheimer's while someone is still alive. For a younger person, an extensive work-up may be more helpful than for someone in her 80s or 90s. On the other hand, an adult child of someone experiencing dementia-like symptoms may want to know whether in fact her parent has Alzheimer's, as a predictor of the likelihood of her developing it. Again, a thorough neurologist can explain your options and make recommendations.

As someone's dementia progresses, it can become more complex to keep track of her medications and her baseline in terms of cognitive functioning and disposition. Here is a vignette from Alyson about the detective work required if a medication falls through the administrative cracks.

AN UNEXPECTED DIAGNOSIS
Vignette #1

One day, I get a call from Dr. Jane, who visits my mother, Caroline, at her memory care community every week. Dr. Jane tells me that she has just been informed that Caroline hit her physical therapist at her last session. *What?!* Caroline, who is in her early 80s, is usually engaged and polite, even gracious, despite her moderate dementia.

Caroline had recently undergone shoulder replacement surgery, because her chronic shoulder pain was exhausting and depressing her. After a short postoperative stay in a skilled nursing facility, she had returned to her memory care community. Dr. Jane recommended a visiting physical therapist, so Caroline doesn't have to be transported anywhere. The sessions seemed to be progressing well, until the day Caroline struck at her therapist. Thankfully, the therapist wasn't hurt. *But what is going on?!*

Caroline's shoulder no longer seems to hurt, but Dr. Jane has observed that Caroline is lethargic, not as upbeat or as verbal as usual. Dr. Jane and I agree that hitting her therapist is seriously out of character for Caroline. Dr. Jane suspects that something else is definitely going on, and she offers to take Caroline over to her primary care physician ASAP. I accept. The doctor examines Caroline, orders some basic tests, and promptly discovers that Caroline's hypothyroidism is raging.

How can this have happened? Caroline has taken thyroid medication every day for decades. Prior to Caroline's admission to the hospital for her shoulder surgery, a list of her daily medications and medication allergies had been provided as requested. Caroline's care community sent the initial complete list to the hospital, but either the discharge planner at the hospital, or the discharge planner at the skilled nursing facility, neglected to include Caroline's thyroid medication on the list that accompanied Caroline back to her memory care community. The nurse at Caroline's care community neglected to compare the new list to the original list, and thus Caroline's thyroid medication has been dropped from her daily regimen.

Thyroid disorders, both hypothyroidism and hyperthyroidism, can cause significant changes in cognitive functioning. Dr. Jane and I surmise that Caroline, at the moment of striking her physical therapist, simply hadn't been able to easily articulate her physical discomfort, so hitting the therapist was the quickest way she could convey, "No, stop, that is hurting me." Caroline was on defense, not on offense. Neither Dr. Jane nor I mention the incident to Caroline, and Dr. Jane discontinues the physical therapy sessions.

Caroline's primary care physician immediately gets her thyroid medication back in her daily regimen, but it takes several weeks for her thyroid levels to build back up and her lethargy to lift. Poor Caroline. I talk myself out of impotent rage and into simply feeling grateful for Dr. Jane's vigilance.

Misinterpreting behavior can have dramatic, even dire, consequences. You can read more about this in Chapter 5, *Decoding the Languages of Dementia.*

Chapter 2 is about early-onset dementia. Until recently, this has affected relatively few people, but it is on the rise, due at least in part to the population bump of Baby Boomers. If you are inclined to skip Chapter 2 for now, we suggest that you simply read its two vignettes and the final paragraph in the chapter (p. 29), *Finding a Neurologist*, before moving on to Chapter 3. These provide a practical foundation for the book's main topic: talking and listening to people with dementia.

2

Acknowledging Early-Onset Dementia

EARLY-ONSET DEMENTIA IS ON THE RISE. Most specialists in the medical community attribute this not simply to increased testing and awareness, but to actual increased prevalence. This is due at least in part to the population bump of Baby Boomers.[15] This chapter looks at people whose lives are being disrupted early by cognitive impairment. The challenges, and long-term impact, of early-onset dementia are in several key ways more complex than when dementia develops in an older person. They are, however, identical in one key respect: Dementia is a disease, and not the fault of the person who has it.

This book focuses on how to communicate with people living with dementia. Until fairly recently, dementia in older people was described as senility, which seems to have carried less stigma than a diagnosis of dementia now does. Grandma acting a bit gaga and becoming forgetful was not nearly as alarming as her being diagnosed with the D-word. Many people—though not all—with early-onset dementia realize that "something seems off" even before their family or colleagues sense this. Because of the stigma surrounding the idea of dementia, some people try to cover their growing confusion and forgetfulness.

Let's say that you may be anxious about your own moments of forgetfulness, and are uncertain what to do about them. You may vacillate between wanting to confide in someone and hoping these forgetful moments are just temporary and will go away. What goes on inside your brain a million times a day is invisible (unless you are undergoing a medical test). So, unlike a mole or a bump, or an ache or a cramp, you cannot pinpoint where your problem is. You cannot see it, you cannot touch it, so you may be tempted to ignore it or to hide it.

The differences continue. If you seek treatment for your toothache or chronic back pain or occasional insomnia, your practitioner is going to recommend or prescribe some course of action, be it a pill, physical therapy, a test, or a procedure. However, if you acknowledge your "brain pain," you may feel that you're letting the cat out of the bag or the fox into the henhouse. But, in fact, not consulting your doctor to learn what is going on is simply counter-productive. Your confusion and/or forgetfulness and/or short temper may well not be early-onset dementia: you may have a vitamin deficiency, which can be addressed; you may be stressed or depressed, which can be addressed; you may have an infection, which can be addressed.

In fact, depression frequently accompanies dementia, but treating only the depression, without acknowledging the dementia, will give less than the best possible outcome. However, if your doctor suspects that you may have early-onset dementia, and refers you to a neurologist, see this as an opportunity to better understand what is happening inside your head, and to ask questions about what you can do and what you can expect.

THE MANY LAYERS OF EARLY-ONSET DEMENTIA

A diagnosis of early-onset dementia usually provokes feelings of loss not only for Robin but also for her partner, or adult child, or other significant caregiver: loss of options, loss of independence, and, most painfully, loss of the future that has been planned for, saved for, and anticipated. If Robin is diagnosed in her 40s or 50s— or even when she is 64, and not yet eligible for Medicare—she is probably still in full swing:

> **DR. JANE SAYS** | A woman in one of my support groups, whose husband has early-onset dementia, told me, "He feels invisible, like he's losing himself. That's how he described it to me. I think he's frightened that he is going to disappear."

1. Robin may still have children at home. If so, the household will be down a parent, in terms of domestic duties as well as parenting. Additionally, the children may become embarrassed, confused, and/or frightened by Robin's changing behavior, including forgetfulness.

2. She may still be working. Robin may sense that her job has become more challenging, but is not sure why. She may feel she is struggling, but does not want to confide in a colleague or her partner. If she is the primary breadwinner in the household, this becomes even more frightening.

3. Robin herself is going to need some help. Her partner, if she has one, will have to juggle working, keeping house, taking care of the children, all on top of taking care of someone who is quite possibly in denial about her increasing limitations.

Regardless of her specific circumstances, Robin may well consider herself independent, self-sufficient, and competent. This self-perception is part of who she is, and her reactions are those of an independent, self-sufficient person, even as her dementia progresses and her abilities decrease.

In this chapter, two vignettes illustrate how to help someone who is experiencing cognitive mishaps, and especially ways to encourage the person to seek a diagnosis and treatment without making them feel anxious, betrayed, or embarrassed.

WHO'S PICKING UP LAUREN FROM SCHOOL?
Vignette #2

Deborah and Tom are in their early 50s and have two children, Lauren, who is 14, and Adam, who is 16. A couple of years ago, Tom noticed that Deborah occasionally wrote checks that bounced, and he realized that she was no longer actually balancing their checkbook. He didn't say anything about her bookkeeping mistakes, but he offered to take over this task, and Deborah was delighted. Since then, all has appeared "quiet on the homefront."

Deborah is an accomplished stay-at-home mom. She is very organized, a fantastic cook, and an enthusiastic driver to-and-from their children's after-school activities. She also volunteers twice a week at a local food bank. One day, Tom gets a call from daughter Lauren, who says, "I have been waiting for Mom to pick me up from school, and she's not answering her cell." Tom makes an excuse for Deborah and assures Lauren that he can pick her up himself within half an hour. He immediately calls Deborah to make sure she is OK, and is so relieved when she answers. She seems surprised that Lauren expected Deborah to pick her up from school, but Tom knows it had been arranged that morning. On the phone, Tom attributes the mix-up to Lauren's adolescent brain and assures Deborah that he can pick their daughter up right away. The next week, the same mix-up happens again. Tom is able to pick up Lauren, and he doesn't confront Deborah...but he is now slightly on his guard.

Tom starts keeping a list of incidents when Deborah's behavior is not business-as-usual. Over the next month, he realizes that, even though Deborah is pleasant and engaged, she is not really able to solve problems or anything unexpected. It's almost as if running the household has become too much for her. He doesn't say anything to Deborah, because he doesn't want to hurt her feelings or alarm her. Though Tom feels awkward going behind his wife's back, he feels he should do something. So he calls their primary care physician for advice.

The doctor listens carefully to Tom on the phone, and suggests that they simply make an appointment for the two of them. That evening, Tom mentions to Deborah that he has made appointments for both of them to have their annual check-ups with their primary care physician.

At the appointment, the doctor asks Deborah and Tom individually a range of questions (known as a mini-mental status exam), and Deborah scores in a range that is concerning to the doctor. Deborah doesn't realize this, but Tom does. The doctor recommends that Deborah see a neurology specialist, who will assess her brain functioning and make recommendations. At this, Deborah loses her composure and starts to sob. The doctor and Tom both comfort Deborah. Tom offers to make the appointment with the specialist, and to accompany Deborah. She starts to cry again and insists, "I'm fine! Why are we even talking about this? I don't need to see a specialist!" The doctor downplays the situation, saying that Deborah is obviously stressed, and that perhaps the specialist will suggest supplements to restore her good humor and optimism.

Tom now feels less alone on this, because their doctor has seen for himself how compromised Deborah has become. On the drive home, Tom suggests to Deborah that perhaps the doctor is wrong and Deborah is right, and that going to the neurologist for a consultation is a good way to prove this. Deborah is delighted that Tom is "siding" with her.

PRACTICAL POINTS

1. Remember that you are not the doctor. Make finding a good neurologist your absolute priority. You can ask your primary care doctor for a recommendation, or you can call your local Alzheimer's Association for a referral, or you can consider consulting a life care manager. (You'll find listings at www.caremanager.org.) A neurologist

can order appropriate tests, then provide a proper diagnosis, and discuss supplements, medications, and other treatment.

(2) Focus on what Deborah can do; remember to compliment her and to thank her. Try to avoid criticizing her for the tasks or problem-solving she is increasingly unable to do. Above all, do not harp on things that she forgets. Telling Deborah that you just told her something two minutes ago is completely unhelpful. It may make you feel better for a few seconds, but then you will feel guilty or unkind, and Deborah may be confused or hurt.

(3) Look for ways to lighten Deborah's load. She wants, as we all do, to be successful. She wants, as we all do, to feel successful. If you simply implement a new normal and stick with it, Deborah may adapt to it fairly easily. Routine is reassuring for people at all stages of dementia, so if you can casually adopt some structure(s) in your day and your week, you can remind Deborah of what is coming up. You can also make a paper calendar to keep by wherever Deborah eats breakfast, and update it continually.

(4) Be patient and kind—not only in your heart, but also in your tone. Deborah is an adult, not a difficult child to be disciplined or scolded. She may or may not be aware that she has some sort of problem. You do not want Deborah to worry that *you* have a problem, that *you* are telling her things that are not true, or that perhaps she cannot trust *you*. You want to keep Deborah as physically safe and as emotionally secure as possible.

HELP YOURSELF REMEMBER!

It makes great sense to jot down your observations and concerns as you go. It is easy to think you will remember what happened last night when you broached the idea with Robin of going to a memory enhancement class or a support group, but your recollection will be at its most reliable if you write it down as soon as possible. If you have to think back and reconstruct, you are more likely to overlook some details, or, frankly, to editorialize. Additionally, recounting stressful anecdotes will stress you each time you tell them. It is better for you to write them down and basically be done with them.

JOAN BECOMES AWARE
Vignette #3

Mark and Joan have been married for five years. It's a second marriage for both of them. Joan is 60, and Mark is 62. Neither of them had children. Joan still works as a freelance writer, and Mark still runs four successful dry cleaning shops, which he's owned for the past 25 years. Mark manages the couple's finances, including paying all the bills. He normally sorts through the mail when he gets home, so Joan just puts it in his office.

Lately, Joan has noticed that Mark has lost some weight, and she realizes that for several weekends, he hasn't been coming into the kitchen to make himself anything for lunch. She doesn't mention the weight loss to Mark, or the fact that she's noticed he's not eating lunch. She starts casually offering to make his lunch when she's making hers, but he usually declines, sometimes dismissively. "No, thank you, Joan. If I wanted lunch, I would make it!" She thinks he is under more stress than usual, as it has been difficult to find and keep good employees. Within a couple of months, Joan will suspect that employees are leaving because Mark has become unpleasant to work for.

Joan and Mark have dinner together every evening, and Mark's appetite seems fine. But when they talk about their respective days, Joan notices that Mark repeats the same "news" in the course of a single meal. So, it's not only that he's repeating himself, but Joan also starts to wonder whether what he's recounting has just happened, or whether in fact, it happened some time ago, or not at all.

Recently, Mark misplaced the keys to his car, which it turned out he had left in the car in the driveway. Joan decides she needs to say something. She gently tells Mark that he doesn't seem as upbeat as usual, and that he seems stressed. She suggests that they make an appointment with his primary care doctor, and Joan is hugely relieved that Mark agrees with no resistance.

At the appointment, the doctor listens both to Mark and to Joan, and he agrees the stress of Mark's work may well be behind the changes in his mood and causing increased forgetfulness. He recommends that Mark not skip lunch, and he prescribes antidepressants.

Fast forward two months. Joan goes into Mark's office to vacuum, and she picks up a stack of papers Mark has left on the carpet. Right on top is an urgent letter from their bank to the effect that their checking account is in the red! The letter is dated an entire week ago. What's more, it seems that several checks Mark had written have bounced. Joan decides to sleep on this, as she's not sure how to broach it with Mark. She's not particularly worried, because she knows they have plenty of money.

At dinner that night, Joan mentions that she noticed the letter from the bank, and Mark blows up, claiming the bank has made a mistake. Well, Joan realizes that this is unlikely. She lets Mark say he will take care of it, but in the morning, she calls the doctor to voice her concern. The doctor suggests that Mark see a neurologist for a consultation as soon as possible, and he gives Joan a referral to to someone he knows.

That evening, over dinner, Joan casually asks Mark if he had a chance during the day to call the bank and the mortgage company. He makes an excuse about how busy a day it was, and assures her that he'll take care of it in the morning. Joan says, "Fine," and then tells Mark that she is concerned he's still under too much stress. She admits that she has called his doctor for a referral to a neurologist, to see what they can do to make things easier for Mark to manage. Mark is not at all pleased, but Joan is able to put a positive spin on the upcoming appointment, saying perhaps the neurologist will be able to offer some supplements to help Mark feel less overwhelmed.

PRACTICAL POINTS

(1) Remember that you are not the doctor. Make finding a good neurologist your absolute priority. You can ask your primary care doctor for a recommendation, or you can call your local Alzheimer's Association for a referral, or you can consider consulting a life care manager. (You'll find listings at www.caremanager.org.) A neurologist can order appropriate tests, then provide a proper diagnosis, and discuss supplements, medications, and other treatment.

(2) Keep notes as you go. Be observant about behavioral, grooming, or cognitive changes you notice, and make sure to jot down dates. It is easy to think you will remember what happened when, but having dates will make it possible to organize your observations chronologically. If you prefer to keep your notes on the computer, make sure they are somewhere that Mark won't find them. If you prefer to keep your notes in a notebook, ditto.

(3) Let Mark feel that he is still in control. Also take steps to protect your finances. The more you automate bill paying and other banking functions, the easier it will be for you to monitor things without Mark's feeling that you are checking up on him or undermining his authority. Having Mark use only one or two credit cards will, again, allow you to see what he is spending and paying. (You may be able to decrease the limit without needing Mark's approval.)

(4) Simplify! The less you need to monitor or "reconstruct," the less resentful you will feel, and the more time and energy you will have for being patient with Mark and enjoying his company.

A dedicated notebook is an excellent practice, if you are someone who writes by hand. If you prefer to type on your computer, make a folder and be sure you keep ALL your notes in it. Either way, date your entries and documents, including the year, as an additional easy way to sort. And be certain to keep your notebook or your computer files somewhere that Robin will not come across them, accidentally or deliberately. Also be cautious when you email: Protect Robin's identity and make sure you are sending your emails to the right recipients. It is easy to click on or type in the wrong name(s), with very unfortunate results.

REACHING OUT TO A CONFIDANT

Trying to take care of Robin is a very big job to tackle alone. You may want someone to talk to, ideally a professional, about your feelings as well as about making a short-term plan and a longer-term plan.

If you are Robin's partner or adult child, you will probably feel the loss of Robin as your confidant. A replacement confidant will provide a sounding board so you don't need to keep your feelings and doubts bottled up. Many resources exist, and the ideal is to find one trustworthy professional to provide guidance as your situation progresses. It is remarkably valuable to have someone for the long haul, who knows the background you have shared, to whom you can ask questions and express your uncertainties.

Healthcare professionals—including gerontologists, social workers, life care managers, psychologists, and psychotherapists—all have the benefit of experience. You want someone who is familiar with the many facets of dementia and its unpredictable progression. Even though each person's dementia is somewhat different, there are similarities, and a professional will be far less surprised than you are.

A professional can still be compassionate and comforting, but also has a degree of detachment, an objective and wider lens—which you may be able to cultivate. This can be quite therapeutic for you. Look for someone who is a licensed clinician, preferably with a master's degree or other advanced degree or professional certification. Robin's primary care physician may be able to recommend someone in his or her own practice (such as a physician's assistant or nurse) or to suggest someone they have referred other patients to.

> **A note of caution:** Referral agencies tend to advertise and to sloganize. They may seem friendly and eager to take the burden off you, but bear in mind that these agencies aren't experts. They earn their fees by referring prospects to specific communities with which they have a contract. In a sense, the agency is the marketing or sales arm for certain facilities, with a vested interest, rather than your best interest, in steering you to them.

Alternatively, you may prefer not to confide in a professional, but rather to someone in your family, or to a member of the clergy, or to another close friend. And this is certainly better than keeping it all to yourself, though these people do not have the expertise or breadth of experience that might be most helpful to you. You are not just looking for sympathy (It is NOT all about you.), you are looking for guidance. This situation does not have a simple solution; it will evolve, so you will need a thoughtful plan that can be revised as circumstances change. Professionals who have been down the early-onset dementia path can advise you regarding taking care of Robin today and down the road.

ROOTING FOR A ROUTINE

Having a routine and a daily schedule can go a long way toward helping Robin, or someone with more advanced dementia, feel she has something to get up for and look forward to. Although the dementia itself will not improve, Robin's confusion can be minimized by having a sense of structure to her day.

A routine can provide a real grounding and a mental comfort, whether or not Robin is still working. Having a schedule on paper each morning to refer to is remarkably reassuring—you do not have to keep it in your head or to look at your phone, you can simply look at the schedule. Some people with early-onset dementia are able to make the schedule themselves; others are not, but may enjoy being consulted about what to put on the schedule. Additionally, the schedule provides an in-the-moment topic of conversation.

It is probable that you will need to adjust what you talk about as Robin's dementia progresses. This is not always easy, but talking respectfully and constructively with Robin is one of the most positive ways to preserve your relationship and help her feel less insecure and more confident.

GIFT YOURSELF A NEW PEER GROUP

Whether you are Robin's spouse, child, or close friend, consider attending a caregiver support group, which can provide a sense of belonging to a non-judgmental community of people walking in shoes similar to yours. The support group can also be a sounding board where you will hear the concerns and strategies of other caregivers. You can find support groups near you at alz.org or through your local church, synagogue, or mosque. Sharing your challenges, frustrations, and successes can be hugely therapeutic.

The support group's facilitator typically offers an objective, informed opinion and can advise and provide direction. You will widen your perspective and may even make a pal or confidant with whom to keep in touch between sessions. Dr. Jane has facilitated an ongoing series of support groups for many years. Caregivers can drop in just once, or for several consecutive weeks, or sporadically over several months. Some people find it helpful to attend regularly for a very long time.

FINDING A NEUROLOGIST

Some neurologists specialize in particular aspects of dementia treatment. It is a definite plus to work with a neurologist who will recommend proactive steps for someone with early-onset dementia. Some neurologists practice a more holistic approach to treatment options than others, including supplements, nutrition, exercise, and cognitive activities. Ideally, the neurologist you work with also stays current with diagnostic developments in neurocognitive disorders and clinical trials. For example, researchers are looking at what role estrogen levels and hormone replacement therapies play in the higher incidence of Alzheimer's in women.

3

Accepting a New Reality

PEOPLE WITH DEMENTIA live in the moment. Robin can have many great moments during her day. She can, in fact, enjoy the same great moment more than once. And even if she does not remember exactly what caused her moment of pleasure or feeling of connection, the positive emotion or glow will linger.

Dementia will have profound effects on Robin's cognitive abilities and her overall health—in addition to, most obviously, her memory. Robin may be unaware of her limitations or her diagnosis, or both. This truly does not matter, so you do not need to remind her of these.

We find the analogy of faulty wiring helpful when trying to describe Robin's brain (which is where her dementia actually is). When wiring is working properly, you flip the switch and the light comes on. If the wiring or the bulb starts to fail, the light may flicker when you flip the switch. You may try jiggling the switch, and the light might come on right away, or, seemingly mysteriously, in a couple of minutes. When you are with Robin, you can try flicking and re-flicking, because she will not remember.

This vignette from co-author Alyson Kuhn illustrates how she changed her approach, in a matter of moments, to entice her mother to have lunch.

LADIES WHO LUNCH
Vignette #4

I am living with my mother, Caroline, in her home—the home where my siblings and I grew up, the home in which I am increasingly uncomfortable leaving my mother alone for long. I work out of the house, so I'm there a lot during the day.

It is a weekday morning. My mother has taken to spending much of her day in bed, dozing, reading, and watching TV. And, I suspect, wondering what has happened to her active life.

She has fallen twice in recent months, once in her bedroom and once getting out of the shower, miraculously missing a tile ledge by a couple of inches. In both instances, I have had a very hard time helping her get up. We are lucky that she has not sprained or broken anything on her descent—and lucky that I have not injured either of us trying to hoist her up.

Both times, my mother has minimized the incidents, being a great sport, and I play along. She obviously did not fall on purpose, and telling her to be more careful seems semi-pointless. I do not want to frighten her with dire eventualities, but she is increasingly unrealistic about her physical limitations. She remembers being able to look for something under the bed, or to hop in and out of the shower, but she does not remember that she should not try it now. I remember both falls vividly, but suspect that my mother may truly have already forgotten them—which is not necessarily a bad thing.

Anyway, on this particular morning, my mother stays in bed. She has not gotten up for breakfast, and now it is getting toward lunchtime. She is going to be stiff, weak, lethargic, and possibly a bit dehydrated. I want her to get up and eat lunch. I know that I have a higher likelihood of success if I entice rather than boss. I go into the kitchen and assemble a huge salad. I arrange a plate for each of us, and I set the table in the dining room. I stick my head into my mother's bedroom and say, "It's almost lunchtime. Are you getting hungry?" She replies, "No, I'm not really."

Scare tactics will be counterproductive and hurtful. And it would be absurd to deploy the "I've slaved over a chilled salad bowl to make you this food" argument. My mother is a grown-up, used to making her own decisions about what and when to eat. She still has a great appreciation for good food, especially if it's attractively presented. I need to capitalize on this.

I say, "Oh, OK. I've made us each a salad. We can put yours in the refrigerator for later. I haven't put the dressing on yet. But would you like to come and keep me company while I eat mine? I'm hungry now." She says she would be delighted to, and gets right up.

She does a brief toilette, and by the time she walks into the kitchen, she is looking forward to having lunch together. She exclaims over the beautiful salads and promptly asks if I have put water on the table yet. I haven't, so she does. We enjoy a lovely lunch together, and she compliments me on how delicious everything is. After lunch, she offers to take care of the dishes if I need to get back to work. I say, "That would be terrific, thank you." She thanks me for lunch, and we are both so happy in the moment.

PRACTICAL POINTS

(1) Think about the outcome you want. Being right per se is not the goal. In this instance, I want Caroline to have lunch, preferably not in bed. In another instance, I might want her to shower, take her medications, walk a bit, or drink a glass of water. The secondary goal is that I hope she will feel pleased, or at least not displeased, to have done whatever it is.

(2) Present whatever it is in a positive light. It is counter-productive to set yourself up for a power struggle or a confrontation. Instead, create an opportunity for Caroline to enjoy the moment: to feel in control, useful, or engaged.

(3) If at first you don't succeed, try again, by rephrasing your question or suggestion. A *No* from Caroline at noon will not necessarily be

a *No* five minutes later. She most likely will not realize that you are repeating yourself, or asking her the same thing in a different way.

④ Giving Caroline a different decision to make, may make a big difference in her response. For example, Caroline said she was not hungry (so, not the response I was hoping for) but she was pleased at the prospect of keeping me company while I had lunch (closer to the response I was hoping for).

⑤ Acknowledge, but only to yourself, that you can help Caroline change her mind by redirecting her. You both win when you succeed.

Living in the moment can be a positive thing. Many of us strive to develop or rediscover our own ability to be present in the moment, to not multitask, to not think about the next thing *(Will I have time to return that call?)* or the immediate past *(How could I have forgotten to pack that?* or *Why didn't I say I needed to get off the phone?)* Meditation, yoga, mindfulness, and other practices have gained great popularity in the West as antidotes to the anxieties of modern life. Many experts feel strongly that stress contributes to dementia. Minimizing Robin's stress may well help you minimize your own, not only with regard to Robin, but with regard to other aspects of your life.

> **Let's consider:** that Robin's sense of the "present" can change literally from minute to minute.

If Robin has mild cognitive impairment or early-stage dementia, she may well be aware of her memory problems, and this awareness can exacerbate the situation and lead to depression and agitation. (Chapter 2, *Acknowledging Early-Onset Dementia,* discusses this in detail.)

JOINING ROBIN WHERE SHE IS

Robin automatically achieves being present by default. As Robin's dementia advances, her base level of mental stress may actually decrease because she lives primarily in the moment.

Robin's sense of self may well be her younger self, and she may often respond and react from that point in time. This is one reason many people with dementia complain that they do not belong in a program or a community with a bunch of old people. Telling Robin that she is old, as old as most of the "old people," is not helpful to her. It does not matter for Robin's mental or physical well-being how old she thinks she is. And, if she thinks about it at all, she will mentally adjust your age to fit her scenario. Robin's past may indeed be her present. She may think she is still 21. Do not take it personally—and do not correct or contradict her. Make Robin's quality of life your focus; find ways in which you can help her engage and feel like she has a purpose.

> **DR. JANE SAYS**
>
> Practice marching to Robin's drum. You cannot entice or trick her to march to the beat of *your* drum.

You can actually learn to be better at being present for yourself, by meeting Robin where she is, in her reality. Confronting or contradicting Robin with "your reality" can be frightening and confusing for her. If you persist in telling Robin things she thinks are not true, she may worry about *you* or begin to fear she cannot trust *you*. No matter what you want Robin to do or to understand, it is counterproductive to try to bring her back to your reality by correcting or condescending. Instead, practice meeting Robin where she is, both in time and place. Where she is may change, not just from day to day, but from moment to moment.

By joining Robin where she is in time, you will make things easier for both of you. For you, learning to embrace the moment with meaningfulness is key. Robin is not thinking about the future or the past, unless you engage her in a conversation about her memories. What Robin remembers of her past is only important if she enjoys talking about it. The future really only exists for Robin once it becomes the present. This is not to say that Robin cannot look forward to things. She can, but only if the anticipation or expectation becomes part of her present. And giving Robin hope is more than important—it is invaluable for her well-being.

For Robin, her immediate past may well be a blank. She may not remember what she had for breakfast, or even whether she had breakfast. Remembering what she ate is not important for Robin's well-being, but it does matter that someone actually knows if Robin had breakfast—or took her medications—and approximately when. If Robin's short-term memory is so impaired that she cannot remember when she last ate, she is at physical risk for cascading side effects: lethargy, dehydration, dizziness, an increased risk of falling, and even malnutrition. If you have had breakfast with Robin, you can easily and casually cue her about this. Similarly, if a caregiver tells you that Robin has had breakfast, but Robin is claiming she hasn't, you can also cue Robin about this without directly contradicting her. One easy solution is simply to redirect Robin, by saying, "Oh, I'd love to have breakfast with you. Shall we do that after we take a walk in the garden?" And unless Robin is obese or has diabetes, it is actually fine for her to repeat a meal if she is still interested—it gives her energy reserves. However, unless Robin brings up breakfast again after your walk, let it go.

Robin may make up stories, and her stories serve a purpose for her. Many times, the story is a way of seeking peace or a way of fighting fear. These stories are not fibs or fantasies to Robin. Your task is to affirm the delusion if it is a positive one. Conversely, if Robin is having a paranoid or frightening delusion, your task is to "move the needle off the record." Here is a wonderful example of a joyful delusion: Nearly 95 years old, Virginia reminisces, "I recall feeling so happy when President and Mrs. Bush needed a place to stay while they were visiting Philadelphia. We had room, so they spent the night at our home." An affirming response could be, "Wow! That must have been really exciting to have the President and Mrs. Bush in your home." And Virginia will feel validated.

Robin's distant past—her childhood, her adulthood, her career—may be vivid or vague. Prompting or coaching her to remember is not helpful. It is actually hurtful, and it may undermine Robin's sense of self. Someone living with dementia can continue to lead a fulfilling life in the moment. What matters is that she feels her life is purposeful and meaningful. What matters is that she is content as much of the time as possible.

KEEPING ROBIN'S HISTORY ALIVE

You can talk comfortably with Robin by keeping her dementia front-and-center in your own mind, rather than tiptoeing around or denying it. This does not mean that you should share your communication strategy with Robin. Confronted with Robin's diagnosis (of which she may well be unaware, and that's fine), you may be inclined to focus on her physical safety and well-being but then neglect her non-physical care needs. You will have a much more pleasant time with Robin if you can move past being afraid of the reality of her dementia.

For Robin, a treat can be the same thing, day after day, week after week, as her short-term memory continues to fade. Enjoying an ice cream cone or reminiscing about old photos, time and time again, is something Robin can look forward to. It does not have to be a huge production or indulgence. It can be small, and it does not even have to be fulfilled. The prospect of having her favorite ice cream cone or spending time looking at photos creates a happy moment for Robin. The simplest pleasures from earlier times can be re-introduced and re-enjoyed, even if Robin is no longer very verbal. (In Chapter 5, *Decoding the Languages of Dementia*, you will find several techniques to help you maintain your patience in the face of seemingly endless repetition of Robin's questions and concerns.) You can easily make room in Robin's present for important parts of her past. Her sense of the past is somewhat fluid—she may have retired years ago, but still has vivid memories of that part of her life and may well have retained some of her skills. Following are two examples of honoring someone's past.

> Betty lives in a memory care community. She played basketball in high school, and Dr. Jane and Betty's son wonder if they can rekindle Betty's love of basketball in some active way. Dr. Jane brings in a bucket and a basketball, and devises a game in which she holds the bucket, and gives Betty the ball to toss in. Betty enjoys this so much that Dr. Jane goes out and buys Betty an actual basketball hoop on a stand, which they set up together in Betty's room. Week after week, Betty is delighted to rediscover this game, which she very much enjoys—and is good at.
>
> Helen now lives with her daughter Erika. Helen had a successful career as a real estate broker. Some days, she thinks she is still selling property; other days, she thinks she is semi-retired. Either way, it is easy to engage Helen in conversation about real estate. She may or may not be able to give good advice, but she will think she is, and she will take pleasure in feeling useful. As an interesting aside, Erika comments to Dr. Jane one day that Helen seems to have become nicer now that she has dementia. Erika asks Dr. Jane if this sounds crazy, and goes on to confide that she feels closer to her mother now than she did growing up. Dr. Jane confirms that

she has seen this happen in quite a few families. She encourages Erika not to try discussing this mellowing with Helen, but simply to enjoy their time together in the present. (The "brain breakdown" of dementia can also cause the opposite effect; some formerly gentle people become like bears!)

CONTENTMENT COMES IN MANY FORMS

By drawing on elements of Robin's past, you can create little pockets of time where she is comfortable and content. As mentioned previously, sometimes you succeed, and sometimes you do not. The following true story is a wonderful example of recreating past happiness.

A banker contacts Dr. Jane about one of his older clients, a woman named Ruth, who has no children. The banker is about to retire, and he is concerned about Ruth's well-being at home, even though she has a private caregiver. The banker arranges for Dr. Jane to visit Ruth, who is isolated at home and very bored. In addition to her dementia, she is depressed. On Ruth's mantel is an old photo of her little dog, who had passed away many years earlier. Dr. Jane asks Ruth a few questions about her dog, sees how Ruth lights up, and goes right to the SPCA to pick out a dog for Ruth, one that resembles her dear departed doggy. Ruth immediately knows that the new dog is her dog. The dog thrives under Ruth's love, becomes hugely devoted to her, moves with her to a memory care community, and, when the time comes, is constantly at her bedside during the last days of her life. After Ruth's death, one of her caregivers adopts the dog.

> **DR. JANE SAYS**
>
> One day I asked Grace, a patient with dementia, "How do I slow down time?" Without missing a beat, Grace said, "Focus on what you are doing right now."

Brian, who is 72, has Alzheimer's disease, and he has lived in a memory care community for two years. He has confusion and profound short-term memory loss. Brian's lifelong passion has been fishing. Now, he would benefit from feeling he has a purpose in life—but it would need to be refined, in view of his dementia. Anita, his social worker at the community, meets with Brian weekly. One week, they begin to plan a fishing trip together. They discuss the details, from selecting a date to deciding where to go and what kind of bait to use. What matters is that Brian feels excited and happy to plan a fishing trip. It is the planning that is most important, not whether he ultimately goes or not. A combination of remembering real fishing trips and planning new fishing trips (that won't really happen) works just fine for Brian.

Over the years, Dr. Jane has found herself in many situations where this kind of creative problem solving is helpful. You too can experiment in ways that feel comfortable to you. Try offering a comment or making a suggestion to improve Robin's mood or decrease her anxiety—even if you are not certain your idea will work. If at first you don't succeed, you can try and try again— because Robin will not remember from one minute to the next.

You want Robin to feel she is succeeding in the world around her. You can use your creative thinking to find ways to help her feel valued and productive. Let's say Robin is a retired high school teacher who also served on the boards of various non-profits. If she believes she is going to a meeting with her colleagues, this notion is exactly what you want to encourage. You can also propose various actual tasks to help her feel useful, such as folding clothes with you, simple sorting, or opening the mail. (Robin doesn't need to read or take any action with the mail, simply to open it and stack it, and put the envelopes in recycling.)

> **Let's consider:** Robin can be appreciative, and she can be loving—but she cannot be accountable.

Be patient with yourself as you feel your way forward. Robin is not thinking about your plans or your feelings. She is only aware of her own needs and emotions. She is completely self-focused, and you should not take this personally. Robin does not mean to disrespect you, and she would be hurt or mystified if you accused her of this. Robin's behavior does not mean that she doesn't care about you.

This vignette from Alyson recounts the afternoon of her mother's eightieth birthday celebration.

CAROLINE'S BIG DAY
Vignette #5

My sister Nancy and I have jointly proposed a birthday party as "an idea," to which our mother has responded enthusiastically. Caroline's dementia is progressing fairly slowly: her short-term memory is pretty dim, but her social skills are still great, and she is generally engaged. We plan an afternoon celebration at a restaurant she loves and invite the entire extended family.

The afternoon of the party, I arrive to pick up my mother, who is sitting comfortably in an armchair, fully dressed, looking lovely, but she has completely forgotten about the party. When I remind her, she says, "Oh, I don't really feel like it. I'd rather just stay here." Well, that of course is not an option, but I say, "Oh, okay." We chat for a couple of minutes and then I say that I think I'll go next door and see what her neighbor Jack is up to. She says, "Fine, darling," and I do in fact go next door.

We have invited Jack to come with us to the party, and he has accepted, but he has forgotten (He had a stroke a couple of years ago.), and at this moment, he doesn't feel like it. I say, "Oh, okay. I'll let Caroline know—she'll be sorry you'll miss it. We'll be having fabulous cookies for dessert. Would you like us to bring you some?" He says that would be nice, and I say we'll see him later.

I have been gone perhaps five minutes. I announce to my mother, "Jack is feeling tired this afternoon. He apologizes for not coming with us, but says he'd like to take a little nap, and he'll look forward to hearing all about your party when we get back. I told him we'd bring him some cookies." Then I ask, "It's nice out, but do you think you'd like to wear your black corduroy coat, in case it's chilly when we leave the restaurant?" She agrees that the coat is a good idea, freshens her lipstick, and gets ready to go. *Whew!*

This is definitely one of those days when I think of Caroline's dementia as faulty wiring in her brain. I do not remind her, I do not criticize her, I just try jiggling "the party switch" from a different angle.

At the party, everyone is delighted to see Caroline and compliments her on how lovely she looks, which she does. She is charming and chatty and enjoying herself. Once we have progressed to the cookie platters, our uncle stands up to sing our mother's praises and share a few reminiscences. Then Nancy makes a beautiful tribute and toast. I am standing behind Caroline's chair, and she whispers to me, "I would like to speak now."

I am astonished, but Caroline is an accomplished former debater and a lifelong public speaker. I simply say, "Great, will you be okay standing up to make it easier for everyone to see and hear you?" She says, "Of course," gets to her feet, and proceeds to speak fluidly for several minutes. She graciously thanks everyone for coming and says how much it means to her that all the children of her generation of cousins have come together to celebrate her birthday. She also talks about the importance of family. When she is finished, she simply sits down, and we all applaud. My sister and I are holding back tears. Mine are a mix of relief, pride, and bittersweet nostalgia.

When I get our mother home, she pronounces herself "happy as a clam" but tired. I suggest that we can open all her cards and packages before I leave. She gets into bed, and we open everything. She is delighted by the CDs of old musicals, and we put one in her bedside player. We agree that it has been a perfect afternoon. I tell her again how beautifully she spoke, kiss her goodnight, and leave. I admit to feeling triumphant. We have given her the best birthday gift: an opportunity to bask in love and limelight. She has unexpectedly risen to the occasion, shining brightly herself.

PRACTICAL POINTS

(1) Bear in mind that a *No* at 2:00 is not necessarily a *No* at 2:30, or even 2:10. If at first you do not succeed, reframe your request and try again. It will be counter-productive to point out to Caroline that she has changed her mind. Sometimes, a *No* is simply a way of showing a sense of control or independence. It does not really mean no. Conversely, sometimes a no means yes. So, if you are not sure, try approaching from a different angle.

(2) Remember that everyone (including you) has good days and bad days. Dementia is unpredictable, inconsistent, and mysterious. Caroline can seem much higher functioning on Wednesday than she does on Friday. If you only see her on a good day and she feels the need to "show well," you will not have a realistic sense of how she is doing.

(3) Play to Caroline's strengths. The party was an occasion where she was extremely comfortable, and remembered her lifelong love of public speaking. She did not have to plan the party or invite the guests; she did not even have to remember that there was going to be a party. She looked lovely, was completely confident, and felt she had something significant to impart. The cards and CDs she received provided happy tangible reminders of a glorious occasion.

EXPLORING NEW WAYS TO COMMUNICATE

The golden rule of communicating with Robin is: you cannot reason on your terms. If you try, you will lose. The happy corollary is: you may be successful if you learn to reason from Robin's point of view. Even if Robin is no longer very verbal, her comprehension level may be fairly intact. Her cognitive limitations actually may make it easy for you to do many kindnesses for her—and she registers these, even if only momentarily. Again, the glow will linger.

One of the symptoms of dementia is declining verbal ability, not just in terms of remembering specific events or people (or their names), but also in terms of finding the right words to express thoughts and feelings. Not everyone with dementia experiences this symptom, and some of the people who do, only experience it episodically, in one or more forms: word-finding problems, mixing up words, decreased vocabulary, vagueness, and word substitutions. Some people will invent words, or use a word to mean something totally unrelated, or even whip up a "word salad" that you cannot actually deconstruct. It is pointless to correct or contradict. In most instances, simply going along with the statement will do the trick. If you feel it is important to confirm what Robin is trying to tell you, ask a non-judgmental question using the correct words, and chances are good she will follow

> ### DR. JANE SAYS
>
> It is easy and empowering to give Robin choices. Keep them simple and clear, so that Robin can easily follow and decide. You can also voice your own preference.

your lead and respond in a way you can understand. If you ignore Robin, she'll feel unheard, and probably anxious and confused. You cannot chastise her for bad behavior or for acting like a child. She is doing her best in the moment to communicate.

Sometimes, Robin may feel that it is too hard to find the words she wants, or she may feel angry or frustrated at being misunderstood. She may even become physically aggressive when she is in physical pain and cannot express that verbally, so it is always advisable to start by seeking a medical explanation for behavior changes. Aggressive behavior may well be a sign that another physical problem, such as a urinary tract infection or medication imbalance, exists.

As Robin's dementia progresses, physical expression may replace verbal expression as her way to convey either positive or negative thoughts and feelings. Behaviors that seem childish or anti-social— hitting, pushing, kicking—are not necessarily violent responses in their intent, but rather Robin's attempt to communicate in the moment. Robin, at a loss for the words to express her frustration or discomfort, may spontaneously hit, as shorthand for "Don't do that, it hurts," or "Leave me alone." It's extremely important to Robin's well-being, and to your own, that you try to avoid misreading her behavior. In Chapter 5, *Decoding the Languages of Dementia*, you will read about the risks of misinterpreting behavior in the vignette "Saving Sara: A Psychiatric Drama."

On the upside, Robin may become much more comfortable than she used to be with being touched by caregivers. Many people with dementia undergo significant changes with regard to their sensitivity and responsiveness to being touched. You may find Robin very receptive to being hugged or having her shoulders rubbed or her hair combed. Her personal boundaries, and sense of her own space, are less defined than they used to be. Being touched or held, whether it is clasping her hand or elbow, helping her put clothing on or take it off, may make her feel delightfully secure. These forms of non-clinical touching feel very different than having your pulse taken. Holding hands, giving a hug or perhaps a neck rub, are non-verbal ways of saying, "I hear you."

Let's consider: Sometimes, simply leaning closer can be helpful. It conveys "I want to connect with you."

Your own body language is something Robin can still completely understand. So, if you take a bossy stance with your arms crossed while you are explaining something, Robin may get defensive or anxious. If you use a disapproving or baby-talk tone, she will also sense that, and it will not help you achieve whatever you are trying to communicate.

By paying attention to Robin's behaviors, you can find cues and clues to her unmet needs. Remember that Robin may not be able to understand your direct question. Or, she may simply have lost the ability to correlate cause and effect. For example, she is shivering, but she doesn't connect this to being cold. It's an isolated feeling, rather than the result of a temporary circumstance she can remedy. She may or may not be able to find the words for sweater or jacket or cold. If you notice that Robin is shivering, you can try observing, "It's gotten a bit chilly in here. Would you like to put on a sweater?" If Robin responds in the affirmative, you can ask which sweater she would like, giving her an opportunity to be in control. She can respond, she can be decisive, but she is no longer able to figure out what exactly she needs in order to be more comfortable.

4

Getting Help & Being Helpful

DENIAL AND ITS "EVIL TWIN" GUILT may undermine your good intentions to care for and to communicate with Robin. These emotions are common reactions to Robin's diagnosis of dementia. In a very real sense, you are confronted with a "double whammy": the potential stresses of caring for Robin and the stigma associated with dementia, a degenerative disease. Robin has needs, which will continue to evolve—and you have needs as well. Balancing them can be a challenge.

THE EDGE OF GUILT

Even if you love Robin deeply, guilt will look for a way to worm its way in, as you consider solutions that you realize Robin may not be pleased about. Moving beyond the guilt will make it easier for you, as will practicing self-forgiveness. If you have been cast into the role of caregiver out of obligation, or by default, guilt will compound your resentment. Perhaps you are divorced, but your former spouse has no one else to turn to. Perhaps your family member with dementia is a parent or sibling with whom you have not had a close relationship. You can learn a lot from Robin about being in the moment. You may surprise yourself by becoming more patient and by taking real pleasure in your momentary victories.

Your feelings of guilt may make it tempting to procrastinate. Alas, procrastinating will make you feel guiltier. A classic guilt-inducer is that Robin may not want any caregivers in her home. Try to approach this from her perspective: she may not think she needs help, or she may simply not like the idea of having strangers in her home bossing her around, handling her things and asking her questions, messing up or incorrectly cleaning *her* kitchen. You, however, may get to the point where you are desperate to get help for Robin—because it will provide relief for you and keep her safer. And, in fact, having help may be a relief for Robin, if you are able to present it in a way that she can understand and accept.

Bathing is an excellent example of a caregiving quandary. Robin may no longer like to bathe, and this is a real problem for which you need to find a work-around. Many people with dementia become frightened about showering in general. They may wonder what they are doing in the shower. Robin may forget literally from one day to the next how to operate the shower. She may remember going into the shower by herself, but not remember what she does next. So, she becomes shower-shy, and you feel guilty about needing to trick or cajole her into bathing. In Chapter 7, *Gauging When Home (Alone) Is Not Enough*, you will find a list of clues to look for, indications that Robin is or is not bathing (or being bathed).

You may also feel guilty that you can't fix Robin's dementia. You cannot make it go away, and you are feeling _____ [choose one or more emotions: alone, angst, despair, frightened, grief-stricken, guilty, helpless, overwhelmed, paralyzed] about trying to take care of Robin and to anticipate her continually evolving needs. Her dementia is interfering with your schedule, your mental energy, and your sleep. But Robin is exempt from realizing this. You may also be feeling guilty because you are feeling tired of dealing with Robin's care and her decline.

> **DR. JANE SAYS** | Fibbing to Robin to enhance her well-being can be useful. This may be a shift from the honesty you have enjoyed with her in the past. Now, you are getting honest with yourself about Robin's limitations and her new needs.

DENIAL: THE FOURTH D-WORD

Dementia offers fertile ground for denial. This powerful coping mechanism is a protective way to avoid acknowledging the truth or reality. Robin has the luxury of not even knowing that she is in denial; you, however, cannot afford this luxury.

For most family caregivers, denial is a big stumbling block. It can stem from a lack of communication, which is exacerbated if you live far from your loved one. The confusion of dementia does not necessarily show up in a phone conversation, particularly in the early stages. And, if Robin senses that you are testing her, she may well be able to cover her forgetfulness.

Your denial may also be a form of self-preservation, fear of what the future holds for Robin and for you. Denial can manifest itself as brushing away Robin's behaviors as simply being normal signs of aging. It can manifest itself as delaying getting a diagnosis or as a reaction to the diagnosis. When family members are not all on the same page, the script of "What's Next for Robin?" can quickly take on aspects of a bad soap opera. Here is how George's two children resolved their awkward philosophical differences about next steps for their father.

MISSION IMPROBABLE: MOVING GEORGE ON THE QT
Vignette #6

George, the father of William and Marianne, is 79 and lives on his own, in the family home in Detroit. George's wife, Kristina, died several years ago after a long battle with cancer. William and Marianne realize that the time has come to move George to a memory care community, and William has taken the lead on looking at communities right in Detroit. They have not told George yet (and that's a later part of the story). William finds a relatively new community for George that he likes a lot.

William sets up an appointment for himself and Marianne to meet with the director, but the morning of their meeting, Marianne does not show up. William tries calling and texting her, with no success. Meanwhile, the director makes several great suggestions about managing George's move, but William is distracted by wondering if Marianne is OK. When he tries her again, she picks up. She assures him she is fine, but that as she was getting ready for the appointment, she started feeling dizzy, and when she lay down, she fell asleep. He asks when they can get together so he can tell her about the director's recommendations. She says she'll get back to him.

The next week, Marianne is a no-show to help William empty out George's storage space, and the week after that, at the last minute, she calls to say that something has come up and she can't meet him at the furniture rental place. (The director of the memory care community has recommended they not bring any of George's furniture from home initially. Instead, they will rent things that fit beautifully in his new room. This will allow George to still envision his home as intact.) William is fit to be tied. Marianne has terrific taste, is normally so dependable, and now is flaking out on him. He asks her what is going on, and she admits, "I'm sorry, I really am. I feel like we're deceiving Dad about his future, and I'm just not comfortable with what we're doing."

William takes a deep breath and asks, "But you still agree we're doing the right thing? That this is what's best for Dad?"

Marianne says, "I do. I really do, but I just can't be part of it right now. Is that OK?"

William replies, "Of course it is. So I have just one request: Please don't do anything to undermine me. We want to get through this with as little upset to Dad as possible. I do not want him to see me as the villain who kicked him out of his home. I wish we could tell him the truth, but he couldn't understand it."

Marianne says she understands perfectly and she agrees—and she adds that, if it is OK with William, she would just like to keep her distance until after the move. She proposes calling George to say she has a cold and that she does not want to risk giving it to him. (George's sense of the passage of time is already compromised, so Marianne is confident she can use this excuse for the three weeks until the move.) William responds that this sounds like a really good plan. And he means it.

The next day he sends an email to his ex-wife, Jamie, explaining what is going on. Jamie has kept in occasional touch with William, and with George, since the divorce. And George is totally comfortable with Jamie. William says he has a big favor to ask: Can Jamie possibly meet him at the memory care community the day the rental furniture will be delivered? She can tell the men where to place things, and send back any pieces that are not needed. And perhaps even come shopping with him for incidentals. He wants the room to look like it is in a nice hotel. Jamie immediately says that she will be delighted to help. William sends an email to Marianne to let her know that plans are progressing smoothly. He says he will keep her in the loop, but that he will not ask her to be involved until after the move.

PRACTICAL POINTS

(1) Realize that you may find yourself suddenly feeling like you are an only child. If a sibling you were counting on does not come through to help you, he or she is probably having an issue that has less to do with you and more to do with the discomfort that dementia often gives rise to.

(2) Try to think outside the "usual suspects," and you may find other people delighted to help you, because they are less emotionally involved. Play to people's strengths.

(3) Find someone to confide in, perhaps in a support group. Consider keeping a journal, even if you normally do not. You may discover, somewhat to your surprise, that you derive comfort, confidence, or strength from writing about your caregiving experiences, whether to let off steam or to update others on your team.

Denial is a two-sided coin, in the sense that Robin may not be in denial in the same way that her family members may be. However, Robin does not necessarily benefit from being stripped of her protective denial. Most people with dementia are not aware of their limitations, and may even be offended at the suggestion that they have memory loss. Robin's denial may lead her to believe, "There is nothing wrong with me. I am not forgetful, you are!" You cannot argue or change her mind on this. Medical and social experts are divided on whether it is better to inform Robin that she has dementia, or not. Many people with dementia sense that something is wrong *(I can't remember, I don't feel like myself.)* but confronting someone with a clinical diagnosis is not, in most cases, helpful.

Some people are aware of their dementia and can even help their family members prepare for future care. Planning groups exist to help people newly diagnosed to understand and evaluate their future care options.

Let's consider: that honesty is not the best policy if it makes things worse.

Family members' denial, not necessarily of Robin's diagnosis, but of what is helpful to her, can make things more difficult for her and for the people trying to care for her. Behavioral symptoms are easier to ignore than overt physical symptoms. If Robin were coughing or limping, there would be no doubt that action was required. However, if Robin is confused or forgetful, it is easy to brush her lapses aside.

Consider Karen, who is in denial that her 78-year-old mother, Jean, should move from assisted living to a memory care wing in her retirement community. Karen desperately wants Jean to be the independent, competent mother she has always known, so she overlooks Jean's increasing confusion and memory loss. She literally cannot see that Jean needs more help, that she will be safer and less stressed in an environment designed to support her and to compensate for her memory challenges. Karen is depriving Jean of the treatment she needs—which she would never do if Jean had a sprained ankle.

Often, a family may become focused, even hyper-focused, on one parent, the one whose memory problems are throwing everyone for a loop. The "healthy" parent is not the focus of the adult children, who may even assume that the non-memory-loss parent will become the primary caregiver.

Take Rose and George, for example, who still live in their own home. They are both in their 80s, and they have three daughters. Rose and George also have a small black poodle, whose name is Dee Dee. Several strokes over the past few years have left Rose with significant memory problems, and George is her main caregiver. Daughter Sara is visiting one Saturday, and she stays with Rose while George goes to pick up Dee Dee from the groomer (where he had successfully deposited her that morning). When George arrives back home, he has with him a black standard poodle—clearly not their dog. As the dog runs nervously around the house, Sara barrages her father, "Whose dog is this? How could you bring the wrong dog home? And where is Dee Dee?!" George tries to explain, "I was not paying attention. This dog is a black poodle, and I just thought it was our dog." This incident is a glaring, upsetting reality check for the adult children, who have been focused on Rose and her needs, but in denial that George cannot care for her on his own. They simply haven't seen that their father is having his own memory and confusion challenges.

Desensitization is different from denial. Often, caregivers (professionals as well as family members) experience temporary emotional burn-out, which may manifest itself as ignoring Robin's questions, assertions, or physical cues. This is doubly confusing to Robin, who is unable to understand why she is not being heard or helped. The confusion makes her feel anxious, suspicious, and disregarded. Sadly, people with dementia are often made to feel invisible.

DESTIGMATIZING DEMENTIA

The stigma surrounding mental illness in general and dementia in particular is long-lingering and slow-dissipating. Up until fairly recently, most people were not comfortable talking about dementia.

Many of us, when we forget something, jokingly refer to having an Alzheimer's moment or a senior moment. Under the humor lies either relief because we know we do not really suffer from memory loss, or anxiety that we may in fact be at risk for memory loss.

Robin may feel shame if she is aware of her cognitive slips and may start to avoid social interaction that might expose her forgetfulness. For example, someone who loves to play bridge may decline invitations to play. Robin may go from seeming normal one morning, to feeling totally lost and confused the next. Or, from behaving normally one day, to exhibiting erratic behavior the next. So, a layer of embarrassment may overlay Robin's ability to ask for help.

Robin cannot help herself to think through her confusion and insecurity about what is happening to her. One of the greatest kindnesses you can do for her is to make her feel that she is still herself, still someone you care about and want to be with. It is particularly sad when someone in Robin's own family is so embarrassed by her dementia, that he tries to hide it from other family members. This is a common possibility, not an imaginary worst-case scenario. Dr. Jane has met quite a few couples, where one partner has been diagnosed with dementia, and the non-dementia partner decides to try and keep their grown children from discovering what is going on. The dementia will become more apparent despite the non-dementia partner's attempts to hide or compensate for it.

For example, Keith and Kathryn are true life partners, married for over 50 years. They have one daughter, one son, and four grandchildren. The grown children and their families live several hours from Keith and Kathryn, who've recently moved full-time to their summer home in a coastal town. Several years ago, the cousins who saw Keith and Kathryn more frequently than their own children did, began noticing changes in Kathryn's personality. Normally demure, Kathryn was becoming very outspoken, sometimes to the point of being argumentative. The cousins also noticed that Keith was taking over the cooking and other domestic tasks. Then, he began keeping the family at a distance and discouraging the planning of visits. The saddest aspect of Keith's denial is that he does not pursue treatment for Kathryn, so she becomes incredibly bored and isolated. Members of the extended family see what is going on, but feel powerless to confront Keith. Poor Kathryn.

Let's consider: that you can't pull "reasoning rank" with Robin.

Robin, despite her increasing mental limitations, is a grown-up. Whether or not you have valued her opinions in the past is beside the point now. Confronting Robin is not constructive or productive, and it can be cruel. To do what is best for Robin, you have to put any resentments and impatience aside. In Chapter 5, *Decoding the Languages of Dementia*, you will read about specific techniques for communicating with Robin to help her feel respected—and to help you feel you are not losing your mind.

You trust yourself to make important decisions all the time, and, as long as you are realistic about Robin's needs, you will be able to make good decisions for her. However, in most instances, you will not have the comfort of candor, which is to say, you will not be able to discuss with Robin the scenarios you are considering— for her next doctor's appointment, or for her next year. Resist the temptation to be frank with Robin about things she cannot understand, particularly concerning her own limitations. You can learn to present (and re-present) an option, a decision, a plan in ways that Robin can understand.

THINGS YOU CAN CONTROL AND THINGS YOU CAN'T

Even if you have arrangements in place and Robin is relatively safe, you will probably have dramas. The emergencies that can arise for Robin are unexpected in ways that are different than what you are accustomed to. You cannot go around constantly on alert, but you do want to be prepared to deal with a mental emergency, which may or may not put Robin at physical risk. Someone needs to be reachable in the event of an incident requiring an immediate response, approval, or authorization.

Make a conscious effort not to feel guilty that you cannot anticipate and control Robin's every move. She could fall at any point (as can older people not suffering from dementia). Robin, however, is particularly at risk for falling. She may need a cane or walker for stability, but the Robin that Robin remembers didn't use one, so Robin will need to be cued matter of factly, time and time again. She can fall in her home; she can fall in a memory care community; she can fall on the way to the doctor's office. You want to be attentive and vigilant, but you cannot put Robin in a bubble. If you confine her to a wheelchair, you are depriving her of independence and exercise, and her dementia may actually accelerate.

It is natural to want to keep your hands on the steering wheel of Robin's dementia, though you cannot steer. For example, a common upsetter of "dementia as usual" is a urinary tract infection (UTI). Robin may or may not be aware of her symptoms, such as itching, burning, or frequent urination. And even if she is aware of them, she may not be able to link them to their cause, or she may simply forget to mention them. Just because she isn't voicing her discomfort does not mean she is not uncomfortable. (There is no clinical data to support our assertion that UTI's disproportionately rear their inconvenient heads on Friday evening or over the weekend, but we have seen it happen time and time again.) If Robin still lives at home, the quickest way to determine whether she actually has a UTI is probably a quick trip to an urgent care clinic. If you are not geographically in the same place as Robin, however, you will need to rely on someone else to sleuth out this possible cause of Robin's discomfort and then to take the next step. Your feeling guilty or frustrated will not make Robin any more comfortable, so use your energy to problem solve instead.

You may find you are losing your patience. You may even find yourself wishing it were over. You may feel you have no time for yourself. For Robin, time is no longer sequential. She will be pleased to see you— and you can put on a happy face, as the saying goes, for a few minutes. Conversely, Robin can sense your stress or impatience or anger, even if she cannot figure out why you are being distant with her, which in turn makes her anxious and depressed. Leave your woes behind and be in the moment.

Robin's dementia cannot improve physiologically, but her functioning, comfort and contentment can, in many instances, improve temporarily, given an engaging environment. Creating positive moments for Robin will make you feel like you are succeeding, and Robin will feel the warmth of your attention.

DR. JANE SAYS

There are upsides to Robin's memory limitations, hard as this may seem to believe. For example, quality time with Robin can be as brief as fifteen or twenty minutes.

BEING COMFORTABLE ASKING FOR HELP

To minimize your feelings of guilt and frustration, a smart first step—for your own mental health as well as for Robin's well-being— is to accept that you probably cannot care for Robin by yourself. Whether you think of it as a team, a village, or a network, building a support system of people who can help you take care of Robin is essential both for her and for you. You will need a team—actually, the ideal to have two teams: one that helps care for Robin, and your personal team that helps you deal with the challenges of caring for her.

If Robin lives with you, you can have an eye and ear trained on her, even when you are engaged in non-Robin activities. However, when you are fully focused on what you are doing at home, or when you are out of the house, Robin is automatically at greater risk for mishaps. Anticipating her needs and ensuring she is physically safe is complex, and complicated by the fact that her mental state can change unexpectedly. At 9 am, Robin may be fine with the idea that you are leaving for work or errands, but as the day progresses, she may become more confused and scared about being alone. If Robin still lives on her own, the risks are even greater.

Friends and other family members may be able to check in with Robin. Some people will be happy to do this, especially if you can give them advance notice and a specific timeframe. You can let Robin know that she will be having company—or even propose that she invite the person (who has already committed to coming over).

However, some people will prefer other assignments, rather than being asked to spend time alone with Robin. Do not add to your guilt by asking people to do things that they are not comfortable doing. And do not add to your resentment by feeling let down. Everyone has boundaries, baggage, or both! Think creatively about other things these people can do to help you: errands, including picking up at the pharmacy; grocery shopping; gardening; and dropping by with Robin's favorite treats. You can help Robin's friends to continue their relationships with her by making it easy for them to do kindnesses for her. If a friend is willing to visit briefly while you are there, you can cue them to follow your conversational lead.

READING, WRITING & REALIZATION

This book focuses on communicating compassionately with people who have Alzheimer's (or another dementia). This topic has not received the attention it warrants, while articles and books about other aspects of Alzheimer's abound. You may be interested in reading more about dementia and caregiving, whether for insights and ideas, or for reassurance and hope. *Other Books You Might Find Helpful*, at the back of this book, presents brief blurbs about several books that contain interesting perspectives and anecdotes about talking and listening to people with dementia.

"Dementia books" tend to fall into one of three main types: personal accounts, popular practical books (including caregiver guides), and more academic books. The latter are often co-authored by an MD and another specialist, and they tend to be dense. Many readers find these helpful, while others find them daunting or depressing. Caregiver guides are self-help books, which is to say that their recommendations tend to be caregiver-centric, rather than dementia-centric. They offer practical strategies for dealing with complex physical logistics and with the stresses and grief of caring for someone with dementia. Personal accounts can be touching, whether they are fiction or nonfiction. If you find a writer whose storytelling style resonates with you, this can be therapeutic and even cathartic.

Enjoying reading about someone else's incredibly difficult day (or night) or improbable series of mishaps, does not mean you are a bad person. As the saying goes, misery loves company! And if you do not want to read about Alzheimer's, that is OK too. Either way, you may find that you derive comfort, confidence or strength from writing about your own experiences with Robin, whether to let off steam, update others on your team, or just to record your feelings.

> **DR. JANE SAYS** | Find an outlet for your feelings and thoughts, whether in a journal, via text, with an email confidant, or just talking on the phone. Don't try to hold it all in.

Be discerning in your quest for help and hope. Websites can make unsubstantiated claims, often supported by statistics with no verifiable sources. Use your common sense. If something sounds too good to be true, it probably is not true. The increased incidence of Alzheimer's has brought dementia to the forefront, in terms of media coverage, literature, blogs, fundraising for research, and a myriad of alternative therapies. The latter include herbal supplements, hyperbaric chambers, brain exercises, and stem-cell treatments. For now, the stigma persists, and unsubstantiated claims proliferate about research, disease reversal, and cures.

Scams targeting older people are notorious, and increasingly ingenious. Robin, in her dementia, is particularly susceptible as her cognitive powers and short-term memory decline. But you may also be vulnerable where Robin is concerned. You may not feel desperate, but you might give a great deal for a solution, or a cure, or a reversal, or even a slowing of the symptoms. You may be predisposed to believe what you wish were true.

HOW SUPPORT GROUPS WORK

Support groups bring people with similar (or overlapping) challenges and concerns together. Do not be too quick to rule out the benefits of having a candid and informative setting where you can share the issues you face—issues you cannot discuss with Robin. Each person's dementia is different. If you pick up ideas in a support group, realize that some will work for you while others may not. Some you may reject out of hand—but you may be pleasantly surprised to find that an approach you would not have expected to work, works beautifully.

If you are taking care of (or anticipate needing to) someone with dementia, a good support group can be a powerful and valuable resource. A search for "forgetfulness support groups" online brings up hundreds of thousands of results. You can instantly narrow your search by adding a city or neighborhood name.

Most support groups are led by a facilitator, often a social worker or psychologist. This person has the benefit of experience, plus clinical knowledge regarding the various types of dementia. You can learn a great deal from a skilled facilitator as well as from the other participants in the group. You can ask questions in a non-threatening, non-judgmental, non-clinical environment.

Caregiver support groups come in various sizes and settings. Finding a group that suits you has several benefits. First and foremost, you will be in the company of people who are going through the same things as you. Friends (and family members) who are not dealing with dementia cannot really understand, no matter how much they love or admire you. They can be sympathetic, but not truly empathetic. Talking and listening to people who "get it" is extremely therapeutic. You will hear other people's stories about their challenges and their solutions. You can compare notes, offer suggestions, and let off steam. You can laugh, and you can cry. A support group is also a great place to share resources and recommendations for personal care providers, communities and day programs, and specialists.

If Robin is already living in a memory care community, chances are good that an ongoing support group exists right there. Trying it is an opportunity for you to meet family members of other residents, which can help you understand their behavior and limitations, and make you more comfortable about interacting with them when you come to visit Robin. The support group may have occasional guest speakers on diverse topics; the leader of the support group will also be up to date about new auxiliary services offered that you might not otherwise be aware of—and how to propose them to Robin (acupuncture and foot massage, for example).

The more knowledgeable you are, and the more connected you become to other people who understand what you are juggling, the less stressed you will feel. In your support group, you do not have to put up a brave front. You can be candid, you can cry, and you will be comforted—even if you are normally reserved. You will meet others who speak your new language, and you may make new friends. Most support groups are free of charge and an excellent investment in your own well-being.

5

Decoding the Languages of Dementia

LARRY IS A RETIRED BOOKKEEPER, still living at home with his wife Rosalie. Recently, he has taken to spending several hours a day shuffling and reshuffling the same piles of papers. Rosalie confides to a friend that this new habit of Larry's is driving her nuts. She says that when she asks Larry what he is looking for, and whether she can help, he actually gets a little snappy with her and responds, "Nothing. I'm fine, dear."

Is there any purpose in Larry's seemingly useless activity? Is he futilely searching for something he cannot find? Yes to the former question, and no to the latter. Larry's behavior does have meaning for him. He finds shuffling and reshuffling his papers soothing and comforting. It is of no importance that he is not accomplishing what we might consider a productive task. For Larry, shuffling his papers is akin to yoga or knitting—both of which are considered acceptable, and even beneficial, non-verbal activities. It is the moment that matters to Larry, not the outcome.

EVERY BEHAVIOR HAS MEANING AND PURPOSE

Robin's behavior can be mystifying and even irritating to those of us trying to communicate with her. Sometimes it is fairly easy to follow or decipher what Robin (or Larry) is trying to say; other times, it is more difficult and occasionally frustrating. The important thing, the thing worth putting your energy into, is responding to Robin in a way that makes sense to her, that satisfies her need or desire in the moment.

Robin is still present, and will continue to be, even in the latter stages of her dementia. Learning to talk and listen to Robin in her world is the key to connecting. Robin may no longer be able to recognize and express her needs, but she still has them—and they won't go away. Your challenge is to figure out what Robin is trying to communicate, verbally and/or non-verbally.

> **Let's consider:** that time is not sequential for Robin.

Robin perceives time and the passage of time differently than we do. This requires some getting used to for anyone trying to care for her, or simply to have a conversation with her. Robin may move the past into the present, adjusting her age backwards in time—and this may become more pronounced or extreme as her disease progresses. This can actually make it easier to engage Robin in conversation and to redirect her attention. She is not going to get irritated with you for repeating something, because each time will be the first time she hears it.

Robin does not differentiate much between events that took place a long time ago and things that happened more recently. She may be able to tell you very detailed stories about the past, but is not able to situate the events along a continuum of time. Robin may remember her 20-something self, without having any idea that she is now actually in her 70s or 80s. She may adjust your age accordingly as well. For example, she may believe that her son is actually her husband. Though this kind of confusion is common, it is particularly upsetting to family members, who feel forsaken or discarded. Remember: This is NOT about you.

These points, which have been discussed in previous chapters, are helpful to keep in mind as you read about the various languages of dementia.

DR. JANE SAYS

Robin's social skills and conversational instincts may stay intact for a long time, even as her memory declines.

(1) Each person's dementia is different.

(2) You'll want to march to Robin's drum. You cannot entice or trick her to march to the beat of *your* drum.

(3) Robin's sense of the present can change literally from minute to minute.

(4) It is easy and empowering to give Robin choices. Keep them simple and clear, so Robin can easily follow and decide.

(5) Honesty is not the best policy if it makes things worse.

DECIPHERING ROBIN'S BEHAVIORS

Dementia can cause a multitude of unexpected—and sometimes challenging—behaviors, resulting from the progression of the disease. Nearly everyone with dementia will experience some degree of behavioral and mood changes. Family members are frequently perplexed by these, asking each other, "How can we get Dad to take a shower when he refuses?" or "Mom cries and yells that I have kidnapped her when she visits my house. What are we going to do?!" Any behavior, no matter how strange or upsetting it may seem to you, is not unique to "your Robin." Even though her actions may be unexpected, uncharacteristic, or generally socially unacceptable, they fall within her new normal. These may include:

1 – resisting care, such as refusing to take medications or to bathe

2 – changes in the brain (delusions, hallucinations, paranoia)

3 – physical aggression (kicking, spitting, pushing, hitting)

4 – responding over-emotionally, such as crying, laughing inappropriately, yelling, or being verbally abusive

5 – hyperfocusing: obsessing, perseverating, becoming unduly anxious

Such challenges, also known as "colorful behaviors," can usually be attributed to one or more of three general causations: (1) physical, (2) emotional or mental, and (3) environmental. Sometimes, figuring out what is bothering Robin is easy, even instantaneous; other times, you may have to explore a little.

> **Let's consider:** Sometimes, offering a distraction or a nap—not unlike restarting your computer—will do the trick to "reset Robin."

PHYSICAL FACTORS

Pain is the prime culprit behind colorful behaviors. For Robin, pain or an illness packs an extra punch if she cannot determine or remember what her malady is. Almost any physical discomfort, from a scratchy throat to a scratchy sweater, can impact her behavior. (You may have read about the behavioral effects of a urinary tract infection in Chapter 4, under "The emotional moving target.")

Robin may be unable to isolate or identify the source of her discomfort, but you often can. If she does not feel well, her proprioception and her problem-solving skills may be even less sharp than usual, until the problem is alleviated, or at least acknowledged and addressed. Even if you cannot instantly solve Robin's problem, letting her know you "feel her pain" and that you are taking steps to make her more comfortable may be the proverbial spoonful of sugar.

A great example of this: Robin does not remember the dental appointment she had yesterday. Her mouth is very sore today, and eating is actually uncomfortable. She says she feels like someone has punched her. She may be lethargic or cranky. She may announce she would just like to take a nap.

What to say: You might matter-of-factly cue Robin: "Oh, you know, I think the dentist mentioned yesterday that you might feel sore today, because of the work he did at your appointment. He also said you did great, and that you won't need to have any more work done." Or, you can skip the dental update and get on with making Robin more comfortable. Either way, some sympathy will go nicely with the hot tea you offer.

What not to say: Reminding Robin that she has forgotten is not helpful. You can cue her, but do not make her feel that she has failed to remember.

What to do: Suggest various pampering remedies that will help Robin physically and emotionally. She may enjoy choosing, or she may prefer for you to decide. You have many options: having a cup of tea (together); wrapping her neck in a soft scarf; holding a hot-pack or cold-pack to her cheek; offering her a little neck and shoulder rub, and discussing what appeals to her for the next meal. You might put in a call to the dentist pronto, to check about giving Robin some Tylenol.

EMOTIONAL & MENTAL FACTORS

Depression frequently accompanies dementia. Stress and confusion may exacerbate both Robin's dementia and her depression. One of the most common behavioral symptoms is *sundowning*. This phenomenon is due to the physiological change that occurs normally in the brain at the end of the day, telling us it is time to go home. For Robin, this can provoke anxiety, aggression or frustration. Although you cannot prevent this mood dip, you can sometimes short-circuit it by giving Robin something positive to focus on. For some people with dementia, behavioral interventions work; for others, calming medications may be effective. Here is a story about Marci, a live-in care companion for Lorraine, who has moderate Alzheimer's.

Every afternoon like clockwork, Lorraine becomes agitated around 4:00 pm, pacing back and forth around the house, looking for her children—who should be home from school by now. (Her children are in fact 30 and 34.) As she begins to shout, Marci helps calm her down by trying various interventions. If one does not work, she simply tries another.

Some days, Marci shows Lorraine childhood photos of her children and asks her about them. Other times, Marci suggests they enjoy some tea and cake while they wait, reassuring Lorraine that the "kids" will be home in an hour or so, because they probably had an activity after school and simply neglected to mention it. If the weather is nice, Marci proposes that they take a little walk outside while it is still light, adding that they may run into the kids on their way home. It never fails that once Lorraine is busy selecting her sweater or coat and putting on her scarf, she is looking forward to the walk and has forgotten about the kids.

Robin can get herself in a state over a perceived threat, or if she is feeling bored, or if she is having delusional paranoid thoughts. She cannot talk herself out of a delusion, because she does not know it is a delusion. She may be prone to perseverating, which is the negative flip-side of persevering. When she gets in a mental rut or loop, she is stuck, like a hamster on a wheel. She may keep looking for the same thing, or worrying about the same thing, over and over and over again. Robin cannot self-soothe.

What to say: Be reassuring and respectful. Mirror back to Robin what she may be feeling, be empathetic, and then quickly redirect her attention to something more positive. Robin wants to feel heard, not pooh-poohed, but you do not need to jolly her or editorialize.

> ### DR. JANE SAYS
>
> For Robin, It's not just what you say, but how you say it that matters.

What not to say: Telling Robin that she is imagining things or getting herself worked up over nothing, is not an effective way to relieve her anxiety. If she is overwrought about something that has happened or that she suspects might happen, her concerns are real. Be attentive rather than dismissive, even if she is having a hard time finding her words. Frequently, you will find a grain of fact in the kernel of Robin's anxiety. You want to get Robin on a positive track.

What to do: You can also help Robin by providing physical comfort: a gentle hug, holding her hand, offering a soothing or nurturing snack, or suggesting you listen to some music together. Your goal is to create a sense of security. Changing Robin's mood is possible. If at first you don't succeed, try again in a couple of minutes.

ENVIRONMENTAL FACTORS

By environmental we mean any factor or influence that is external to Robin. This can be an overstimulating or understimulating environment, or simply a change of routine or surroundings. You want to try to identify possible triggers for her behavior.

For some people who live in a memory care or assisted living community, an occasional or ongoing desire is "I want to go home." The person is not necessarily referring to the home she came from, but rather to a place that makes sense to her, where she feels safe and not threatened by things she cannot understand. This desire commonly arises when someone is sundowning. Remember that "home" is a concept. It is more than the actual house or apartment where someone resides or used to live. It is the place where the person feels comfortable and safe.

For many people with dementia, entering a bathroom or shower can cause increased anxiety, agitation, and fear. It is possible to quickly reduce colorful behaviors by improving Robin's overall sense of well-being.

What to say "I know you're ready to go home now. Could you help me sort your mail, and then afterwards, I'll take you home?"

What not to say "This is your home, Mom. We sold your house last year, remember? You live here now."

What to do Give Robin a change of scene, and a mental distraction, by proposing a walk (or a "tour" in her wheelchair) or a drive. Then, when Robin returns to her room or her community, she will have a sense of "homecoming," of being back where she belongs.

THE THREE R's: RESPONDING, REDUCING, REDIRECTING

Because Robin has a brain disease, it can be tempting to marginalize her as no longer being vibrant or smart or even interesting. This is a disservice to Robin. And, you are short-changing yourself of the opportunity to build a different sort of relationship with her and to enjoy her company. Your mission is to help reduce Robin's negative emotions and behaviors. Some days you will succeed, and some days you will not. There is no silver bullet or magic potion.

Some of our own fears about dementia stem from not understanding the world of the person with memory loss. But some of our fears also come from anxiety about ourselves and the possibility that we may develop dementia. Because our society tends to marginalize people with dementia, we become even more fearful for ourselves. We do not want to be cast aside.

RESPONDING

The following story is a great illustration of deciphering the meaning and purpose of the behavior of someone with dementia. Meet 84-year-old Peter, a new resident in a memory care community.

Peter has vascular dementia, the result of several mini-strokes. Most of the time, he is pleasant and polite, but in the dining room he is a major disruption. Mild-mannered Peter vigorously pounds the table, startling the other residents and causing silverware to jump. The staff has had no success trying to calm him down, and they have all begun to dread his pounding performance. What to do?

A review of Peter's admissions paperwork reveals that he is a retired judge. Pounding the table—in the absence of his gavel—is his attempt to communicate the need for order in the dining room. He finds the dining room chaotic and tries to subdue it, using a protocol that has worked for him for many years. The dining room manager, once he is aware of the cause of Peter's frustration, quickly proposes a simple solution: to seat Peter in a less populated, quieter section of the dining room. The change in Peter's behavior is instantaneous.

The staff, rather than dismissing Peter's behavior as infantile or anti-social, or medicating him for aggression, sought a logical explanation by looking to, and acknowledging, Peter's past.

Let's consider: that dementia should not define the person. The person is still there.

REDUCING ANXIETY

You may feel ill-equipped or unqualified to deal with unpredictable behavior, but learning to respond constructively and compassionately in the moment is easier than you might think. It is not that difficult—but it is frequently counter-intuitive. Think of this as learning a new language. Although Robin may not be able to self-soothe, you can help her by offering comfort or reassurance, rather than by criticizing her behavior.

Colorful moments and challenging behaviors are part of the languages of a person with dementia. It is not helpful to correct Robin's behavior to fit into what we think of as normal. Robin still deserves her privacy, her dignity, her quiet time—but isolation is one of the worst things for someone with dementia. It leaves Robin on her own to try and make sense of her reality.

Almost everyone with dementia experiences psychological and behavioral symptoms, including restlessness and agitation, at some point. Sometimes, such episodes or outbursts can be effectively managed without medication. Do not assume that because these behaviors are related to the disease, the only approach is medication. Conversely, if Robin is in acute distress, and in danger of harming herself or others, medication can be a quick and effective intervention.

REDIRECTING

You can redirect Robin's attention in much the same way a detour redirects traffic away from a hazard. Because Robin's immediate memory is compromised, if you can distract her, it is possible she will not mentally back-track to her starting point. Another analogy we like is that of a stuck needle on a vinyl record—you can pick up the needle and move it forward even the tiniest amount and the music resumes.

Many people become nervous trying to think of what to talk about when spending time with Robin. Whatever the topic, the conversational landscape has to include her. Resist the temptation to talk around her, to tell stories that do not include her, to act as if she were not right there with you. Talking as if she cannot understand, or does not deserve to have a say, is hurtful. She can still hear! Bear in mind that the topics in which Robin is interested will tend to become narrower and narrower. Unlike most of us, Robin is not interested in what is going to happen an hour from now, or tomorrow, or next week.

Chances are good that Robin can understand what you are saying, even if she has difficulty articulating her own thoughts. Just because she is not being very verbal does not mean she is not interested. But give her some time to respond, so she can indicate how she is feeling. You may be short on time, but Robin is not. Even as Robin becomes less verbal, you still have many options for engaging and connecting with her.

Reminiscing is a great agent of engagement. Looking through an album of old family photos is a good activity for connecting with Robin. She may want to tell stories, or she may prefer to listen. You can also get a sense of the progression of Robin's dementia by how she identifies people in the photos.

Cuing Robin is an excellent form of redirecting. Robin may be able to tell you she had a lovely visit, with you or someone else, but not be able to give any details. This does not matter, because you can easily cue her, if this will increase her pleasure: "I'm so glad you found a great vase for the flowers I brought." Even someone who is no longer very verbal can enjoy a visit. Do not feel let down if Robin does not express her appreciation.

Showing affection is another excellent form of redirecting. We are all familiar with the notion that a blind person develops heightened awareness through their other senses. Similarly, Robin may become more receptive and appreciative of touch, even from people she is not particularly close to or has not known for long. She may get pleasure from a hug, a held hand, a mini-massage. Giving Robin a little shoulder or neck rub while she is sitting in a comfortable chair, or even in a wheelchair, is a treat for her—and a way to carry on a gentle conversation, without being face-to-face. This may make it easier for her to gather her thoughts and express them.

Playing music can be powerful. Years ago, Dr. Jane encountered Marjan, a woman with advanced dementia, who had been placed in hospice care. When Dr. Jane first saw her, Marjan was curled up in a fetal position and had begun refusing to eat. Marjan was from Iran, and Dr. Jane was bothered by the quietness, the total stillness, of her room. Dr. Jane thought that Persian music might be a meaningful way to connect with Marjan. She found some Persian CDs in a local music store and returned to Marjan's room with the CDs and a CD player. What happened over the next few days was amazing. Marjan began responding. She woke up! The music touched her sense of self. She reconnected with who she was, through her native music. A part of her became alive again. Marjan's last days were much more peaceful.

THE "*KIND* KIND OF LIE"

This is the expression we use for what is commonly called a "therapeutic fib." As we've said before, and will say again, truth is relative. Telling Robin a hurtful truth is exactly that: it's hurtful. If she has forgotten that her husband died three years ago, there may be no value in reminding her that he has passed on. Allowing her to believe that he is at work, or on a business trip, may well be the better thing to do.

In our opinion, the *kind* kind of lie is frequently the best approach for connecting with Robin where she is. She has a brain disease. Telling her a *kind* kind of lie, or agreeing with *her* reality, is not deceitful. On the contrary, it is compassionate as well as practical. Because you cannot reason with Robin, quite often you cannot be truthful with her. Depending on the topic, telling the truth can bring emotional pain and increased confusion for Robin. The *kind* kind of lie helps reduce her anxiety and challenging behaviors.

> **DR. JANE SAYS**
>
> Telling the *kind* kind of lie should not make you feel guilty.

Let's say Robin believes she is in charge of her memory care community. Every day, she fires the staff. The staff plays along with Robin, allowing her to believe she is in charge and that she has the authority to fire them. This reduces Robin's anxiety and allows her to feel empowered. It is all about letting Robin win! Her delusional thought is in fact a form of communication. She wants to feel in control, as she did when she worked as a successful real estate broker.

> **Let's consider:** that a person with dementia reverts back in time.

Some of us are much more comfortable than others with not being truthful. Being untruthful may go against our core values, values taught us by our parents. The key to becoming more comfortable with telling the *kind* kind of lie is to remember that Robin has a brain disease. Telling, and repeating, a "therapeutic fib" can be a compassionate part of rolling with Robin's reality. Caregivers, because of their experience dealing with many people with dementia, often become creative, and almost intuitive, about how to empower a memory-impaired person. Here is a wonderful example of this.

MARY & HER BLANKETY-BLANK PARENTS
Vignette #7

Mary is an 80-year-old woman with moderate-stage Alzheimer's disease. She has lived in the same memory care community for three years. The staff has been trained to be comfortable and spontaneous in telling Mary and the other residents "the *kind* kind of lie," which is to say, a therapeutic fib. The staff understands that Mary has a brain disease. Her forgetfulness and her confusion are symptoms of her dementia. The compassionate staff accommodates Mary in her world of dementia, day after day.

Toward the end of every afternoon, Mary experiences "late day confusion," which is also known as sundowning. This is not uncommon for people with dementia, and usually lasts a few hours. Low lighting can trigger a sundowning episode; insufficient activity, or over-activity, can also contribute to this. For Mary's well-being, the staff needs to be well trained, in order to prevent her anxiety from ramping up.

Every evening around 5:00, Mary waits by the door for her parents, whom she believes will be arriving shortly to pick her up to take her out for dinner. Her parents have, of course, died decades earlier, but Mary is still young in her own mind. After a couple of minutes, she begins to pace back and forth, becoming visibly agitated. A few minutes later, every evening, a staff member comes over and informs Mary that she has a phone call at the desk.

It is actually one of the nurses telephoning from elsewhere in the community. Mary comes to the desk and picks up the phone, and hears, "Mary, this is the Sheraton Hotel calling. We want to let you know that your parents have called to say they are running late. They won't be arriving at the hotel until later this evening. Your mother asked us to call, so you wouldn't worry. She says to please plan that they will pick you up for dinner tomorrow evening, instead of this evening, at 5:00."

Mary responds, "Oh, my, those #%$&$%! parents of mine... they are always late." She thanks the hotel and hangs up. Mary feels listened to. Her misbeliefs become real. Every evening, a staff member comes over to her as she replaces the telephone receiver, and asks Mary if everything is alright. Mary explains about her parents' delay.

The staff member sympathizes briefly and then asks, "Oh, well, if you aren't going out with your parents this evening, will you join us for dinner in the dining room? And the tables haven't been set yet. Would you like to help us do that?" Mary is back in her present. She feels useful, and she has just been offered two things to look forward to: setting the tables, which she enjoys, and having dinner with her fellow residents.

It would be futile—and upsetting—to try and remind Mary that her parents are dead. Every day, she looks forward to dinner with them; a few minutes after her phone call, she has forgotten her recent disappointment. Mary does not feel lonely or abandoned. She is not isolated; she is in an orderly, familiar, safe place. And she has the residual pleasure of feeling that she is right—even more right than her tardy parents!

PRACTICAL POINTS

(1) Consider the option of not telling the truth. A therapeutic fib can feel awkward if you are the adult child of someone with dementia. Your parents were probably the people who impressed on you how important it was to tell the truth, and now you may feel guilty at deceiving one of them.

(2) Create opportunities for Mary to feel listened to. Most people like to be the storyteller, and Mary's story about her parents is so vivid to her. Reliving and recounting it keeps her parents alive for her, which gives her comfort.

(3) Find ways for Mary to feel needed. Everyone needs a purpose—even if they have a brain disease. Mary's moment-living life is enhanced by opportunities to feel useful; her positive feeling from being useful lingers, even if she cannot remember exactly what she has done to feel useful.

(4) If you get confused with the details of your therapeutic fib, chances are that Mary will not remember exactly what you had said, and you can revise as you go.

YOUR ROLE IS TO ROLL

Flexibility is key to caring for and communicating with people with dementia. Dr. Jane often describes this as being like Gumby: bendable and fluid, and able to get yourself back on track when you feel s-t-r-e-t-c-h-e-d too thin. Alyson tends to describe this as being like the Pink Panther, always able to adapt and come up with a solution, even if it seems wacky at the moment.

Dr. Jane had a client who commented to her one day that being with her husband was like being with a piece of Swiss cheese. Whatever comparison you come up with, you will probably find yourself in situations where you want to scream, or cry, or just close your eyes.

And you can do whatever you want LATER, but not in the presence of Robin. If venting will make you feel better, you might want to find a "venting partner" or a support group. Humor, for you, can be powerful, an antidote to burnout or depression. It is not malicious or disloyal to laugh in private or out of Robin's presence.

As Robin's dementia progresses, or as she experiences disruptions to her well-being, she will likely become less verbal. You will want to be watchful for any behaviors that seem out of her norm, and try to determine what she is trying to tell you non-verbally.

Sometimes, a truly serious situation will arise seemingly out of nowhere, and it may catch you off guard. You can get emotional later, but in the moment, rescuing your Robin will require all your mental energy. The following vignette is a classic example of how easy it is for someone with dementia to fall through the cracks if her behavior is misinterpreted.

SAVING SARA: A PSYCHIATRIC DRAMA
Vignette #8

Sara, Franklin's wife, is 77 and has Alzheimer's disease. Franklin knows it is time to move Sara from their family home to a care community, and Sara's primary care doctor refers Franklin to Dr. Jane. When Dr. Jane meets with Sara and Franklin, she is able to assess Sara's abilities and strengths, without Sara's feeling she is being tested or judged. Dr. Jane asks Sara casual questions about her daily activities, in order to gauge Sara's ability to care for herself. Sara shares with Dr. Jane that she pays the bills, and that she makes dinner every evening, and likes to look up new recipes. It is apparent to Dr. Jane that Sara's perceptions are not current. Dr. Jane does not question Sara further about this.

Later, Dr. Jane recommends a community that will be a good fit for Sara, based on Dr. Jane's experience with the staff there. Franklin thanks her for meeting with them and making the initial recommendation on a good community match. He does not see the need to retain Dr. Jane for ongoing consultation at this point. Franklin, for his own reasons, proceeds to select another community.

Franklin carefully and compassionately plans Sara's move. She is unaware of the upcoming change, and the move goes off surprisingly well. Franklin is pleased and relieved. He continues to live in the family home, which is only a few miles from the community. He visits Sara almost every day. But he only sees what he wants to see—through his rosy-tinted glasses.

Within a month, Sara has become despondent and combative. She cries and cannot be comforted, and she begins hitting the staff. She is unable to articulate what is wrong. The staff seems to be at a loss as to how to deflect Sara's agitation. Imagine how frustrated Sara is by not being able to express herself verbally. One day, she accidentally hits the window with her arm. The staff misinterprets this as suicidal behavior. The immediate consequences for both Sara and Franklin will be horrific.

Sara is sent to a psychiatric hospital for geriatric patients. She spends the next several days strapped into a wheelchair, ostensibly for her own safety. She is over-medicated to control her crying. By the end of the week, Sara has lost the ability to walk unsupported. Franklin is distraught and calls Dr. Jane. To obtain Sara's discharge from the psychiatric hospital, both Franklin and Dr. Jane have to appear in court with Sara. Thankfully, Sara is able to speak the necessary words, "I want to go home."

WIth Franklin's permission, Dr. Jane makes arrangements for Sara to move immediately to the community she had originally recommended. Dr. Jane closely monitors Sara's rehabilitation, which proceeds well. Sara quickly regains her ability to walk; her medications are reevaluated at her new community and significantly reduced. Sara becomes more engaged, less lethargic, and settles in quite well. She is now in a community where she is well taken care of. Her dementia progresses slowly; her gradual physical decline continues, which is part of her dementia disease. Dr. Jane continues to monitor Sara, to assess her well-being and keep an eye on her care. Sara is approaching the final stages of Alzheimer's disease.

Franklin visits Sara on an almost daily basis, and he is able to engage her by talking about their travels and their family, especially their children.

Franklin brings photo albums of their travels to help connect with Sara. Even if she cannot say much, it is obvious that she enjoys looking at the photos, and it is not too difficult for Franklin to reminisce with genuine warmth and affection for the trips and experiences they have shared. When the time comes, Sara will be able to receive hospice care without being moved elsewhere.

PRACTICAL POINTS

① Keep in mind that one size of community literally does not fit all dementias or all Robins. A memory care community, no matter how well-trained and compassionate the staff, is an institutional setting, not a home environment. If you are considering a care community, ask specifically about the things that will matter for your Sara. A seasoned care manager can provide a checklist of quality-of-care factors to look for and ask about.

② Acknowledge that dementia is at the center of whatever problem or emergency you are dealing with. Sadly, there is still a big stigma associated with dementia, but you cannot advocate or problem-solve for your Sara by going around it.

③ Ask questions. To get the best sense you can of what may be behind Sara's behavior, you need to investigate. Sara's neurologist, in an emergency, may be able to either consult directly with you or to recommend a care manager or other specialist (social worker, etc.) to visit Sara and assess the situation. You may find it helpful to flip back to Chapter 1 and re-read the vignette about Caroline, "An Unexpected Diagnosis." Dr. Jane's intervention on Caroline's behalf spared her from much more serious consequences.

6

Empowering the Person Within

EMPOWERMENT CAN TAKE MANY FORMS. Within the context of dementia, this basically involves helping someone feel that he or she is the same capable person they have always been. You can do this by focusing on the person, rather than on their dementia. Doing this is easier than it might seem. Let's consider these two gentlemen and their jobs.

> Richard has moderate Alzheimer's disease and lives at home with Virginia, his wife of 56 years. Richard's daily job is to fold the clean laundry and to go through the mail. These activities keep him busy and give him a sense of accomplishment. The bonus is that Richard and Virginia both have plenty of clean clothes! The mail is a box of various advertisements and other junk-type mail (nothing requiring any follow up; nothing that could make Richard anxious). Virginia brings out the box daily, and Richard spends time going through everything. He has a job and he feels productive.
>
> Felix has lived in a memory care community for the past year. He is a retired architect. Shortly after Felix moved in, the head of the community's maintenance department asked him if he would be willing to join their team. Felix was delighted, and now he walks the perimeter of the community every morning, making

sure there are no structural changes to the buildings. He has a clipboard and a name badge. Felix feels like a valued member of the staff at the community. If he is concerned or curious about something he sees on his rounds, the staff thanks him and assures him they will attend to it and report back to him.

10 (little) BIG THINGS YOU CAN DO TO EMPOWER ROBIN

Empowering Robin is an ongoing approach to helping her feel positive about herself and to helping yourself enjoy your time with her. This is not an exercise or a lesson. Below are spontaneous, in-the-moment ways to engage with Robin. Topics that interest her will give the two of you more to talk about.

(1) Make her feel she is right. Robin is always right, except when what she wants to do puts her in harm's way—in which case you will want to redirect her by proposing an alternative or distracting her. Correcting, contradicting, or arguing is not what you want to do, because you will lose.

(2) Really listen to Robin. What she says provides the best clues to what is on her mind, where she is in time, and how she is feeling. Ask her a gentle question (rather than saying umm-hmm) if you are unsure what she is trying to tell you.

(3) Play to Robin's strengths. Zero in on what she is good at—and set her up to talk about these things and, if possible, to do them. Compliment Robin at every opportunity, to reinforce her sense of self-worth. This also gives her the opportunity to say "Thank you" to you.

(4) Set Robin up to tell you about her history. Try engaging her in conversation about her topics of expertise: her career, her family, her creative pursuits, volunteering, whatever she has been passionate about. Reminding Robin of her gifts is in itself a gift to her.

(5) Help Robin feel useful by thanking her for any kindness she does for you—or for anyone else. She may not be able to articulate how much she enjoyed serving you coffee, so you can add your feelings to your thanks: "I love that you remembered how much I like using those coffee mugs."

(6) Find tasks that Robin can do and that she will enjoy doing. If she is still high functioning, she may be able to execute more complex tasks, and even to organize them herself. If her dementia is more advanced, she will be more comfortable with simpler projects. (Later in this chapter, in "Helping Robin find a purpose" on p. 101, you can read about specific ways and tasks to engage her.)

(7) Emphasize the positive. For example, you can make Robin feel secure and important by saying "I will be here all day if you need anything," even though you will stay for only half an hour. Similarly, you can give her glowing feedback several times (in as many minutes) for the same accomplishment.

(8) Suggest an activity to look forward to. This can be large or small, realistic or not. It is likely that Robin will quickly forget what you had proposed, but the positive feeling of looking forward to something will linger. You can rekindle the anticipation endorphin time and again.

(9) Help Robin feel heard when she comments that she feels confused or not like herself. Sometimes, it is enough to commiserate a bit and ask how you can help. You can offer to help her organize her schedule, her closet, or her desk. Straightening some clutter together may help Robin feel more in control.

(10) We repeat: Make Robin feel she is right. She is always right, except when what she wants to do puts her in harm's way—in which case you will want to redirect her by proposing an alternative or distracting her. Correcting, contradicting, or arguing is not what you want to do, because you will lose.

Robin is indeed the same person she has always been, but now she has a brain disease. You can instill hope in Robin by confirming for her that everything is fine. The idea is to "mirror back" to Robin that she is still herself. She is searching, albeit unconsciously, for a framework to support her, to hold together her identity and sense of self-worth.

A friend recently told us that her grandmother's care community is doing a superb job of encouraging her grandmother's belief that she works there. The management actually gives her a paycheck!

Let's consider: that we can learn from Robin how to be in the moment and enjoy it with her.

FINDING THE TRAIL OF CRUMBS (LIKE HANSEL & GRETEL)

Robin's past is still alive inside her; she has lived her many experiences. Robin has not retired from life just because she has dementia. She may have had a career from which she has retired; she may have raised a family, and her children are now grown; she certainly had friends and interests. You can help her relive the richness of her life, which is the essence of empowerment. Robin is still Robin.

However, the companions, caregivers, and healthcare specialists Robin will encounter may not know about her earlier self. You can empower Robin when you provide glimpses of her past, the things she loves, and what she is all about, to the new people in her present. Bringing her past forward is a great way for you to keep her sense of self alive, to preserve what makes Robin unique as a person. Some days, it may take a little longer to find her, but she is still there. Keep in mind that, as the disease progresses, Robin may have more moments, and of longer duration, of confusion. Be patient. As we have said before, Robin's *No* at 3:00 will not necessarily be a *No* at 3:05.

Caregivers who lack history about Robin are less able not only to value, but also to interpret, seemingly random behavior that may well stem from Robin's past. At one nationwide memory care community, the founders have integrated a meaningful way to include residents' pasts as part of daily life in the community. Just outside the door to each resident's room is a tall glass-sided cabinet with shelves. The management team invites residents and their families to bring photos, keepsakes, small artworks, awards, and other memorabilia, all of which are arranged in the cabinet. This gives the staff and residents a window into each resident's interests and accomplishments. The contents of the display cabinet provide a permanent topic of conversation and pride, as well as a preview of who lives in the room. The items on display keep personal history alive.

This notion of living reminders is also valuable if Robin will be moving from her own home to live with one of her adult children. Robin may not be able to select for herself the things she would like to take with her; you or someone else can do this for her without her participation, and, if need be, even without her knowledge. The prospect of change is frightening to many of us; for most people with dementia, this anxiety is magnified. For Robin, giving up her own kitchen, even if she has stopped cooking, is huge. Having her recipe cards, or photos of holiday meals, a favorite cookbook, or her signature serving piece where she can see them and talk about them keeps these memories and Robin's sense of purpose alive.

For a man, the workbench where he tinkered through the years may have been a significant part of his identity. If he has a toolbox, it figuratively contains years of memories of projects past. Even if he is no longer able to use most of his tools, having them available reinforces his sense of competence and usefulness. (Use of the tools should be supervised, as his motor skills, physical strength, and judgment may be diminished.) A simple build-a-model kit may also satisfy his need to tinker. If he has a favorite model he has assembled in the past, showcasing it on a shelf or mantel provides a moment of recognition and pleasure every time he sees it. In acknowledgment of the "tinker gene," some memory care communities have a men's group whose supervised activities include fixing a toaster or taking apart a battery-powered radio. The fact that the deconstructed appliances never really get put back in working order is totally immaterial. It is the process, the sense of having a project that is so beneficial.

PRESERVING ROBIN'S SENSE OF INDEPENDENCE

Many people with dementia are unaware of their memory loss. Some days, you may suspect that Robin is faking her unawareness, and she may indeed try to cover some of her confusion, but her unawareness of the disease itself is most probably genuine. We are not in favor of attempting to break through her lack of insight by "enlightening" Robin about her impairment. The harder you try, the more resistant she will become. She may also become confused, suspicious, and worried about *you*. If you stop and think about it, what would telling Robin, "You have memory loss." accomplish? Better to ponder how you will work around her limitations, by adapting to them without confronting or contradicting her. Your twin goals are:

> **DR. JANE SAYS**
>
> The basic human need to feel understood is universal. It does not go away when someone develops dementia.

1 – to preserve Robin's sense of independence and control of her own life;

2 – to keep her as safe as possible.

DAVE DOES AILEEN A GREAT KINDNESS
Vignette #9

Aileen, who is 72, lives with her husband Dave in their home in the Midwest. They have no children. Aileen enjoyed a long career as an accomplished seamstress. She had owned a small shop for over 30 years, before selling the business and retiring a couple of years ago. She used the computer frequently in her work, purchasing fabric online, browsing trends, and even managing her own books. Dave has begun to notice changes in Aileen's outlook. She is frequently moody and sometimes short with Dave. He also feels that she is becoming forgetful. One day, Dave points out that Aileen has bought a new bottle of ketchup, which they do not need, and Aileen gets angry and defensive. She starts sleeping in and some mornings says she does not feel like getting dressed. Dave senses that Aileen is feeling she would be "all dressed up with nowhere to go."

Dave wonders how much of her changed behavior is due to the life change of retiring—not going to work any more, not having interactions with customers and suppliers, not having the mental stimulation and satisfaction of running her own business. But, he also wonders if something else might be going on. Could she simply be depressed?

Dave suggests to Aileen that she talk with her primary care doctor. Privately, Dave is hoping that the doctor, who has known Aileen for many years, will see what is going on, and make recommendations. All of Aileen's lab work comes back fine, and the doctor reassures Aileen that she is in good health, but adds that he would like to refer her to a neurologist—a prospect Aileen immediately rejects. Dave does his diplomatic best to explain to Aileen that the neurologist may be able to recommend supplements, physical exercise, and mental activities that might increase her energy and confidence. He offers to come with her to her appointment, and she agrees.

Several weeks after Aileen's comprehensive work-up, Dave and Aileen go back to the neurologist for a follow-up appointment. The doctor explains that the results of the work-up indicate that Aileen's forgetfulness and confusion are due to dementia, most likely Alzheimer's. Both Dave and Aileen are shocked, and Aileen exclaims, "Oh, that can't be true! I don't believe you." She starts to sob, and Dave is speechless.

The doctor gives Dave and Aileen a couple of minutes to compose themselves, then goes on to say that supplements and medications are available to slow the progression of Aileen's dementia. He adds that exercise, diet, and mental stimulation can all help as well. Aileen seems a bit reassured that there are things she can work on, and Dave is privately encouraged. The neurologist writes two prescriptions, including an antidepressant, he recommends an over-the-counter supplement, and schedules a six-month follow-up. Dave asks the doctor if Aileen can call him if she has questions or concerns, and the doctor says *Of course*.

Dave, a civil engineer, decides to retire. He is grateful that he and Aileen can afford for him to stay home. (He knows they will be fine financially as long as she can stay at home, and he decides not to worry yet about what they'll do about future care and its costs.) Dave devotes himself to making Aileen more engaged mentally and more active physically. He misses the stimulation of work and the camaraderie of his colleagues, and so he proposes to Aileen that they invite friends over. Because Dave now has the time to help Aileen with preparations, this is a great success.

Dave notices that the last few times Aileen has sat down at the computer, she clicks on various things, but does not actually get anywhere or do anything. Even after her retirement, she had loved being on the computer, shopping online and surfing the internet. Dave types up some simple steps for logging on, getting online, searching and so forth. He prints them out and places them by the computer. He does not say anything, but is delighted to see that Aileen is able to follow the steps. Now, when she settles in at the computer, she looks like she is getting down to business. She feels successful and independent—and she is eager to tell Dave about things she's seeing online. Dave knows how much Aileen likes to travel and presents the idea of having her plan their next trip to Europe. Aileen loves this idea! Dave realizes this trip may not materialize, but the planning of it gives Aileen a sense of purpose and anticipation.

PRACTICAL POINTS

(1) Gently help Aileen to maintain activities of her own, and to help her cultivate new ones. These will give her something she and Dave can talk about. As Aileen's dementia progresses, what she is able to do may decrease, and it is important that Dave be attuned to this. He can encourage, but he should not push.

(2) Focus on what Aileen can do, rather than on what she cannot. It is much more productive to find work-arounds for the tasks she cannot accomplish. For Dave, now that he is retired, he can offer to do things with Aileen because he has free time.

(3) Explore local resources: day programs, memory-enhancement classes, and volunteer opportunities (animal shelter, hospital, garden shop). The objective is to give Aileen some social interaction, some mental stimulation, and a sense of accomplishment.

(4) Remember that dementia is a progressive disease, so you want to be flexible, in the most Gumby-like sense. Aileen's limitations will become greater over time—what appealed last week may not appeal to her next week. In fact, she may change her mind from moment to moment.

Preserving Robin's sense of dignity is key to her well-being. Inevitably, there will come a time, as her disease progresses, when her physical limitations may require intrusions on her privacy. Requiring help in the shower is a common care need. How you present this will set you up for success (agreement) rather than failure (anger, resistance, refusal). A positive approach is to tell Robin, "After your doctor's appointment this morning, I thought we'd go out to lunch. You have plenty of time to take your shower before we leave. Want me to turn on the water for you?" It is also possible that Robin will become frightened of getting wet. (Read about fear of bathing in Chapter 7, p. 123.) Act as if your assistance is the norm, rather than making a big deal out of it. For example, you may make Robin feel anxious or bossed around if you say, "You should take a shower now, while I'm here to help you. We don't want you to fall." In fact, thinking for Robin, and anticipating her needs, may remind you of taking care of a child, but it is imperative to remember that Robin is not a child and does not usually think of herself as one.

Being overly protective will have the unintended and undesirable effect of reducing Robin's sense of independence. You simply cannot protect her from every risk. It is important for Robin to have a sense of control within reason, to feel that she has choices. Again, how you frame your plan or question will go a long way toward making Robin feel respected and consulted—and increase the likelihood of achieving the outcome you seek. Rather than saying, "It's time to brush your teeth. I don't think you brushed them yesterday." try saying, "Let's both go brush our teeth now. I have some new toothpaste for us to try." Make things fun and mutual—a moment or activity you share—whenever you can.

ADAPTING HOLIDAYS FOR ROBIN

Holidays with Robin will be different than in the past. They can still be a wonderful opportunity to connect with Robin and perhaps to reminisce if she is able. You can still tap her long-term memories of holidays past. She may recall family traditions, which may give her pleasure to talk about. Little things, from planning a special menu to setting the table, can become big things, a project with Robin. Depending on the progression of her dementia, Robin may do better in quieter activities that are not over-stimulating. Let Robin be your guide.

You may find yourself (or Robin's caregivers or friends) thinking of Robin as if she is no longer herself. And in some ways, she is not "the Robin you knew and loved." But she is indeed still Robin.

Holidays in general are a nice chance to express your gratitude to Robin for being who she is. Everyone loves to feel appreciated. And if Robin enjoys being creative, most holidays offer several crafty opportunities. You can make your activities as simple or as elaborate as you think Robin will enjoy.

(1) Decorate. You can do this with Robin in her home, in your home, or in her care community. Solicit her ideas, and, if she is mobile, invite her on a shopping errand. Most holidays come with handy color themes, whether it's red, or red-white-and-blue, or orange and brown. Tactile, as well as colorful, materials may really engage Robin's interest.

(2) Send cards. If Robin still lives in her home, perhaps she would enjoy walking around the neighborhood with you to personally deliver cards. You can make plans in advance with neighbors, without Robin's knowledge, to set a window of time to drop by. If Robin lives in a care community, offer to help her prepare cards to mail to family and friends. Perhaps she would like to make little cards for some of her fellow residents. If Robin no longer writes, she may enjoy being the embellisher: rubber stamping, stickering, coloring, or cutting lengths of ribbon.

(3) Express gratitude (and not just at Thanksgiving). Engage Robin in a conversation about things you are each grateful for. If Robin has a spouse or partner, or a special friend or caregiver for whose company and friendship she is particularly thankful, ask Robin if she would like to write a note, or dictate it to you, for that person. A personal note is a gift that the recipient can enjoy again and again.

(4) Thank Robin. Tell Robin how grateful you are to have her in your life. You can mail her a card well in advance, either directly to Robin (if she still opens her mail), or to a caregiver or neighbor. A bit of advance planning will enable you to figure out these logistics. If you have a photo of a celebration from your shared

past, include a copy with a little reminiscence that brings the memory to life for Robin and makes her feel cherished.

⑤ Engage the senses. Holiday preparations can be a treat for all of Robin's senses, and the residual richness of the experience will linger, even if Robin cannot remember exactly what caused her feeling of extra well-being. Even if Robin is becoming less verbal, her other senses are still receptive. Playing music is a great mood enhancer and an invitation to feel active, even if it is simply in a chair. Smelling familiar scents can be extremely comforting and calming—especially mint or peppermint, or popcorn, or cookies baking, or an aromatic candle (if it is continually supervised). A neck massage or a foot massage, even if Robin has not experienced these in the past, may be her "new favorite thing," especially with her choice of essential oil.

Remember that busy hands are happier hands. Invite Robin to participate in preparations, even if you will want to finesse her work later. Finding ways for Robin to feel useful makes her part of the action. Working with anything tactile, such as fabric, especially if there are buttons or zippers, can bring back childhood memories. Some people with dementia develop a new fondness for having something to hold onto. Items that are soft and cozy, including a pillow or stuffed animal, may provide tactile comfort. Activities involving puzzles and magazines can also be engaging, even if Robin is not actually reading, but is looking at pictures or breaking puzzle pieces apart.

KEEPING ROBIN CONNECTED

As we have discussed earlier, the idea of dementia makes many of us without dementia uncomfortable. You can enrich Robin's daily life by helping her feel there is nothing wrong with her. Arranging for Robin to receive phone calls (which can be brief) and visits (which can also be brief) go a long way toward creating a social life and a sense of activity. Real mail is another familiar form of engagement.

Cards that Robin can read and reread and perhaps display will give her pleasure. If Robin is interested, you can help her send out birthday cards, holiday cards, and even thank-you notes. You can always add a P.S. inviting someone to call or visit.

When you take Robin out for an appointment or a meal, introduce her to the receptionist, the owner of the shop or restaurant, or other people you encounter. Robin can still make new connections, and these are valuable. Some people with dementia retain their social skills, and even their hospitality instincts, long after their memory impairment has advanced. Being gracious, offering to do a kindness, and expressing appreciation are forms of social interaction that feel familiar to Robin, that feel good, and therefore are self-empowering.

If Robin lives in an assisted living or memory care community, or attends a daycare program, she may well make new friends. Take the time to introduce yourself and say how pleased you are to meet them. If you ask them a little bit about themselves, you can chat with Robin about her new social circle. Similarly, the staff in an enlightened care community will find ways to make sure Robin has a sense of belonging. For example, Robin may like to greet people as they arrive in the dining room for meals. It is possible she thinks she actually works there as a hostess. So, the manager can make a name badge for Robin, so she will look and feel like part of the staff. She is connected to her community and feels valued.

The next vignette from Alyson recounts a chance meeting that spontaneously expands her mother's social circle, thanks to the kindness of a stranger who becomes a family friend and an honorary member of "Team Caroline."

MAKE NEW FRIENDS
Vignette #10

My mother, Caroline, has now been living in a memory care community for several months. Our family friend Gladys is my mother's most frequent companion. One Monday afternoon, the three of us slowly walk several blocks to have dessert. I have overestimated my mother's stamina, and she is really tired on our walk back. Then, we see a sandwich board on the next corner announcing that a shop I had wanted to visit, but thought was closed on Monday, is in fact open. It is not out of our way at all, and my mother is game to stop in. I am hoping she might be able to sit down for a few minutes.

The proprietress, Joan O'Connor, introduces herself, and we introduce ourselves as well. I add that my mother lives just around the corner. The front of Joan's shop is at street level, but the back room is up one high step. Caroline realizes she cannot make it up the step and says she'll just keep browsing in the front. Joan immediately says that she has a sturdy little vintage step stool, gets it, helps my mother up, and matter-of-factly asks Caroline if she would like to sit down. Joan offers her a chair, and Gladys and I feel like we have hit the jackpot. Joan mentions how much she likes the Thai restaurant at the corner, so Gladys, my mother and I go for lunch one day.

Over the next few months, Gladys and my mother visit Joan's shop several times; they also concoct a special dish for themselves at the Thai restaurant. Thanks to Joan, my mother feels like a "regular" in her new neighborhood. She feels connected rather than isolated. My mother's mobility continues to gently decline, and she tires more quickly when walking. It has become much easier to take her out in a wheelchair, and Gladys makes these outings as fun as possible.

One afternoon, after a doctor's appointment, Gladys calls me to report that the wheelchair taxi, which had been arranged for, has not shown up to take them back to my mother's care community. They have been waiting on the sidewalk for about fifteen minutes; it is getting chilly; and my mother would like to use the ladies' room. But they are both anxious about missing the taxi. Ultimately, Gladys resolves everything smoothly, but by the time they get back to Caroline's room, not only is my mother totally chilled, but she has also missed dinner. Gladys offers to stay with my mother while she takes a shower to warm up, and I try to figure out how to have a happy ending to this story.

I call Joan, who is just closing up her shop for the night. I say that I am about to ask a big favor, and I explain the situation. I ask Joan if she can call in an order to the Thai restaurant, pay for it, and then walk it around the block and deliver it to my mother's room. She does not hesitate for an instant, asking only if I know what items my mother and Gladys would like. I am relieved. I am touched. I call my mother to tell her that our friend Joan will personally deliver hot Thai food for herself and Gladys in a matter of minutes!

HELPING ROBIN FIND A PURPOSE

Everyone needs a purpose in life, including people with dementia. When we retire, we still need a purpose, and this purpose changes. It is no different for Robin. She needs a job or jobs, so that she can feel empowered, useful, and helpful. Structure and stimulation can promote a sense of purpose. Structure can be as simple as a routine, whether it is implementing a schedule at home of activities and appointments, or encouraging Robin's participation in the activity programming at her memory care community.

You can find purposeful tasks and projects to empower Robin, based on her cognitive abilities as well as her past history. Practical ideas include:

– opening and "sorting" the mail

– looking through grocery store fliers and circling items she would like to purchase. Robin can do this daily, and the purchases do not actually need to be completed.

– folding laundry daily, fresh from the dryer (while it's warm and aromatic) or simply taken from the linen closet

– sorting coins into piles and placing them in plastic baggies

– assembling a snap-together model (rather than one that glues) as a gift for someone

– emptying the dishwasher (if Robin is not a high fall risk).

Here is a brief anecdote about Martin, who unknowingly devises a job for himself. He is asserting himself and feeling useful.

> Martin, who is 91, is a retired businessman with advanced Alzheimer's disease. He had been living in his own home until three months ago, when his family realized that he was becoming too isolated. Now, he has adjusted well to living in a memory care community, and his family visits frequently. Martin's room is decorated with photos of his family, paintings that hung in his home, and several framed awards. The care team often finds Martin's pictures removed from the wall and placed on his bed.
>
> The team manager notifies Martin's family and asks if they have any thoughts as to why he would do this. They are mystified. The next time Dr. Jane visits Martin, the team manager tells her about Martin's behavior and asks what she thinks might be behind it. Her response, which seems obvious once you think about it, is, "Martin does this because he can. The act of taking down his pictures is a behavior that allows him to feel a sense of control and empowerment." He probably does not remember taking down the pictures, but in the moment he feels empowered by his act. The good feeling will linger, which is very important for Martin. The staff simply rehangs Martin's frames when he is out of his room at a meal or an activity.

Think about Robin's life and what has made her feel valued. For example, a mechanical engineer may feel productive tinkering with an old bathroom scale that he can take apart. To end this activity before he becomes frustrated, you can offer to put the box or tray away until later, saying "Now it's time to do [whatever]." He doesn't need to actually put the object back together. The benefit here is that he feels useful and productive.

REINFORCING ROBIN'S EMOTIONAL WELL-BEING

Robin's emotional well-being is as important as her physical well-being in maintaining her sense of independence. Although you cannot control the progression of Robin's dementia, you can control your tone and the way you frame your questions and suggestions. It is easy to overlook Robin's mental and emotional needs and fixate on the physical complexities of her safety. But this is unfair to her—Robin herself is not a problem to be solved. It is her dementia that is "the problem," which you cannot solve or resolve.

Sometimes, Robin is able to sense when she needs to perform to show you that she is fine on her own. The term *showtiming* describes the natural tendency to put our best foot forward in a social situation. In Robin's case, she may actually think she can do everything herself, and she wants to be sure you know she can. It is common for Robin to make up stories about how well she feels. Some days, Robin is "on," seemingly in control of her life, and other days, she may not exactly know what her refrigerator, or her keys, are for. Major lapses like these may indicate the progression of her dementia.

If you only see Robin occasionally, or if you only pick her up when you are taking her out, you may not observe the changes—the subtle and the not-so-subtle—in her competence and perceptions. Some signs are less overt than others. You may not be able to spot these in a single visit, especially if Robin is on her guard to perform well for you. When she is on her home turf, she is probably more competent than when she finds herself in a less familiar setting. Many families fear that Robin will decline mentally if she is removed from her home court. Actually, the reverse is usually the case: Robin will benefit from a structured, orderly, and engaging environment. A memory care community or day program is designed to cognitively benefit people with dementia—much more so than staying at home, where Robin may not only be isolated but also become increasingly bored.

Every kindness does not have a happy ending. For example, Dr. Jane sent flowers to a patient of hers after the woman's husband died. The patient called Dr. Jane the next day to thank her, and then she called Dr. Jane the day after that to thank her again...but when she called on the third day, she angrily asked, "Why would you send me dead flowers? You are fired!" Welcome to Dr. Jane's world.

Yes, Robin's dementia is progressive; no, she will not recover. However, a structured and stimulating environment can improve, for a time, Robin's cognitive functioning, energy level, and mood. A memory care community provides a safe new home where people with dementia have no real-world stress to confuse or overwhelm them. A care community also offers a great deal of sociability and engagement, both with other residents and with staff. Many resources and options exist for in-home care that can have similar goals, from developing a daily routine to improving Robin's nutrition and bathing. Chapter 7 delves into many practical aspects of maximizing Robin's well-being in her home.

7

Gauging When Home (Alone) Is Not Enough

HOME IS THE PLACE where we feel safe and secure. It is likely that some readers will turn to this chapter first, and that is fine. The key principles about talking and listening to Robin, elaborated in previous chapters, are reiterated here. The following two major realities are valuable to keep in mind as you plan and replan for Robin's safety—physical, mental, and emotional—in her home.

(1) Dementia is a progressive brain disease. After Robin has received an actual diagnosis of dementia, she may live for several years, but life expectancy varies for each person. Robin's life will almost assuredly be shortened by her disease. Frequently, family members stall on acknowledging Robin's symptoms or confirming her dementia. The stigma surrounding dementia, the fear of a diagnosis, Robin's possible resistance to going to see a neurologist, and the anxiety about how to afford Robin's care, all contribute to diagnostic and treatment delays that can put Robin at increased risk.

(2) Robin's functioning and her preferences will continue to change. Your notions of what Robin will like (or object to) are based on your memories of her preferences and perhaps on your own. For example, you may assume that Robin will not like the idea of an adult day program. However, you may be surprised to find that she very much enjoys being in a group where she is not being judged, does not have to "get it right," and can express herself non-verbally. Be open minded and creative.

Everyone's dementia is unique. It is tempting to look for parallels and to compare stories, but there is no magic checklist of symptoms and solutions. This book includes many examples and insights, but they should not be taken as pat scenarios or scripts. Compassion and awareness will help you make (and re-make!) a game plan for caring for "your Robin."

HOME IS WHERE ROBIN FEELS SAFE

In planning long term for Robin's care, you will want to bear this in mind. Many of us feel that our home reflects the essence of who we are, both materially and mentally. Home may continue to be just fine for Robin in the early stages, but as her disease progresses, she may outgrow her old home and do better in a new one, such as a memory care community or specialized small home for people with memory loss.

Robin's home is familiar to her. She believes she is in control, because it is her home. She may tell you about doing various things around the house, but her sense of the passage of time may well have blurred, and she may easily interchange things that have happened quite recently with things that happened years ago. It is important not to take Robin's reports at face value, but rather to discreetly investigate on your own to verify.

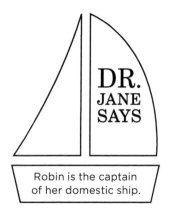

DR. JANE SAYS

Robin is the captain of her domestic ship.

Robin most likely has no insight as to why it has become risky for her to live in her home without help. She will not be able to follow your reasoning that she is not safe in her home, because she has always been safe in it, and she is unaware of the changes in her capabilities. When she looks around her home, she probably sees things in her mind's eye as they have always been. You may see dust or dirt or disrepair, but Robin literally may not. She remembers things as they were, well cared for and maintained. The domestic energy of Robin's past in her home is still alive and vibrant in her memory. If Robin had an office in her home, she may believe that she still works in it, even if she has not used it in a very long time. (We have seen "time capsule" home offices, unchanged and undusted for years.) You cannot be certain of where Robin is in time, and her mental location may change without your being aware of it.

If Robin has had recent mishaps in the house, she most likely does not remember them. She may have left water running, or a burner lit; she may have left the refrigerator door open, or the front door unlocked; she may have fallen and hurt herself. It is unproductive and unkind to remind her of these incidents, because she simply does not remember them. She is not being defensive, nor is she in denial. She will wonder why you are telling her something that she suspects may not be true.

Robin may also develop distortions in thinking, including delusions, hallucinations, paranoid thoughts, and obsessions. If Robin is alone, most likely whatever is bothering her will "ramp up." To Robin, the imagined threat or emergency is real. This poses a serious safety risk for her, as she continues to become increasingly confused. If you are with her when this happens, you may be able to diminish her anxiety by distracting her onto a more pleasurable topic or activity, but it may well be time for a consultation with a psychiatrist or a neurologist.

It is tempting to think you can check in with Robin the way you would check in with someone who does not have dementia. Kay, for example, calls her mother, Katherine, several times a week. One morning, Kay feels that Katherine really sounded great on the phone. She comments to her husband, "Boy, Mom sounded great today. She seems very much like her old self." Two days later, Kay receives a good-neighbor call from the local police department to tell her that Katherine had wandered from her home and had gotten lost. A neighbor, who spotted Katherine walking down the block with socks on but no shoes, called the police. A patrol car came right over, and the officers were able to casually offer to drive Katherine home, where they found the front door wide open. Kay feels like she has just had the rug pulled out from under her.

For Robin, the prospect of change, even the prospect of discussing change, may be particularly frightening. In most instances, it is kinder and more productive not to share your thoughts about possible changes with Robin. The hashing-it-out approach, which most of us use to resolve problems, will not be beneficial for Robin. You may think that consulting her will help her accept the need for change, but it is more likely that you will increase her anxiety and, in the worst case scenario, make her suspicious of you and your motives. If Robin is not aware of her cognitive decline and increasing limitations, your proposing that she might benefit from some help is probably not going to make sense to her. It is likely she will be resistant and even emotional.

The fear of change is not unique to people with dementia. This may be the time to think about your own anxiety around the change(s) that will be best for Robin as her dementia progresses. You may be dreading making decisions that you suspect Robin will be displeased with. You may be panicked at the thought of suggesting she should have help around the house. You may be overwhelmed by the realization that Robin really cannot take care of herself any longer. And, not incidentally, you may be worried about upsetting Robin's "financial applecart."

Robin's specific needs—what provides comfort, security, and pleasure—will change as her dementia progresses. A setting where Robin can feel safe, accepted, and successful is really what she needs. She may not realize how isolated and bored she has become by being home, where she is able to do less and less. You have to be open-minded and a bit experimental. It is not helpful (or kind) to express surprise at Robin's new likes and dislikes—whether she has started working with clay or carrying around a small stuffed animal.

Let's consider: that Robin's short-term memory limitations can work in your favor.

A single *No* from Robin is not necessarily her final verdict. You can ask the same question again, or you can ask a different question about the same thing, and get a *Yes*. Conversely, Robin may be agreeable, even enthusiastic, about an idea at 11:00 a.m., but at 11:15, she (a) has no memory of having agreed and (b) doesn't like the idea at all. You need to go with Robin's flow—and to repeat yourself without saying that you are repeating yourself.

DR. JANE SAYS | If I had a dime for every time I've heard, "But she sounded great on the phone," I could treat every one of my patients to a box of See's candy.

BUT HE SOUNDED FINE ON THE PHONE
Vignette #11

An attentive son   Michael still lives in his own home and is unaware of his dementia. His older son, Peter, lives several hours away. They have a weekly phone call, and Michael sounds fine to Peter, who always asks his father how he is feeling and what he has been doing. Michael is talkative, and if Peter asks something specific, such as what Michael will be having for dinner, Michael's responses seem plausible. Peter last visited Michael a couple of months ago. His sense is that Michael is still managing on his own, although Peter can hear that his father's confusion is increasing.

One day, Michael misses an appointment with Dr. Squires, his primary care physician. The office calls Michael to check that he is all right, and the receptionist realizes that Michael has no recollection of the appointment. She is gentle with Michael, reschedules the appointment, and lets Dr. Squires know that Michael may need some help. Dr. Squires calls Peter (who has medical power of attorney for his father) to report Michael's confusion. Dr. Squires asks Peter if he would like the name of a life care manager who could see Michael in his home. Peter is taken aback and says, "But he sounds fine on the phone." Dr. Squires explains to Peter that having a fresh pair of eyes and ears to meet Michael and casually observe how he is doing, seems like a smart next step. Peter is skeptical, but agrees, so Dr. Squires refers him to Dr. Jane.

Dr. Jane and Peter have a call

On the phone, Dr. Jane reassures Peter that she can, in a short visit, perform a functional assessment of Michael's strengths and weaknesses, and his ability to live safely on his own. Dr. Jane adds that she is accustomed to introducing herself to someone with dementia in a way that does not alarm or threaten, but actually makes them feel comfortable. Peter acknowledges that having a functional assessment makes sense, but repeats to Dr. Jane what he had told Dr. Squires: "He sounds fine on the phone." Dr. Jane says that this is helpful to know, but that it is still quite possible that Michael's domestic circumstances have deteriorated since Peter's last visit.

Peter then asks, "But who should I tell my father you are? How will you be able to visit him without alarming him?" Dr. Jane replies that Peter can tell

Michael that she works with Dr. Squires and that Dr. Squires has asked her to meet Michael (not mentioning the missed doctor's appointment, which Michael probably has forgotten about) to make suggestions as to how he can remain independent in his own home. Peter is fairly confident he can manage this. (And Dr. Jane doesn't tell Peter that she won't be surprised, when she arrives, if Michael has no recollection of who she is or why she is there.)

Peter calls his father and explains that Dr. Jane, a colleague of Dr. Squires, will be coming over on Monday morning. Peter calls Dr. Jane to confirm his success, and adds that his father is always up and dressed by 10 am. Dr. Jane thanks Peter for arranging the visit, and tells him that she will call him on Monday afternoon to report how it went.

Dr. Jane meets Michael

Monday morning, Michael answers the door. He is surprised to see Dr. Jane, so she gently explains, still standing outside, that Dr. Squires has asked her to stop by to visit with him. It is apparent that Michael has no recollection of Peter's phone call last week. Dr. Jane asks if she may come in, and Michael shifts into host gear.

Michael invites Dr. Jane in, offers her coffee, and actually sounds fine, but he is wearing soiled clothing, and the kitchen sink is stacked with dirty dishes. Dr. Jane notices that there is a dishwasher. She asks if she might have milk in her coffee, and when Michael opens the refrigerator, an unpleasant smell is immediately detectable. From the packed upper shelf, Michael pulls out a quart of milk, which is spoiled. He does not seem aware of the odor. Dr. Jane notes, on the counter, that Michael's plastic pill organizer is empty, and that several bottles of medications are sitting around the kitchen, including two on the table, which is also piled with papers. Dr. Jane is able to talk casually with Michael while continuing her mental inventory and then asks if he would give her a tour of his home and tell her about it. He says he would be delighted.

What Dr. Jane sees   The shower is packed full of boxes; the sheets on Michael's bed are visibly in need of laundering; and a stack of bills on the desk in Michael's office actually have a bit of dust surrounding them. Dr. Jane asks him how long he has lived in his home, and Michael replies, "Two years," but Dr. Jane knows that he has lived in his home for 40 years.

After inviting Michael to tell her about a couple of the framed certificates in his office, Dr. Jane thanks Michael for the tour, and says she will certainly tell Dr. Squires how much she enjoyed meeting him.

Dr. Jane reports   That afternoon, Dr. Jane calls Peter, to tell him what she has observed. Peter is, in a word, shocked. He says, sincerely, "But he sounds fine on the phone!" It is clear to Peter, from Dr. Jane's detailed descriptions of the home, that Michael is no longer safe living there on his own without some ongoing help. Dr. Jane recommends possible next steps, and Peter asks if he should fly out as soon as possible. She responds that, if he is able to arrange this right away, it is the best scenario, as Michael really is at risk on his own. Before they hang up, Dr. Jane reminds Peter to bring with him copies of Michael's Advance Directives, Peter's Medical Power of Attorney, and any other relevant paperwork. She then calls Dr. Squires to bring him up to date and discuss care recommendations.

PRACTICAL POINTS

(1) Ask Michael questions that will help you gauge how he really is doing. Try asking the same question more than once to see if you get the same answer twice. Michael will not be cranky that you asked him two minutes ago whether he has had breakfast or what he would like to do today, because he will not remember that you had just asked. You will learn something of value if Michael's answer is not the same, namely that he is improvising rather than really remembering.

(2) Consider engaging a professional—a care manager or social worker—for a consultation to assess Michael's abilities, limitations, and risks. This person can observe, quickly and casually, without Michael's feeling he is being tested or judged, and then make recommendations regarding ways to keep Michael both safe and as independent as possible. If you live locally, you can certainly be there as well. This is a good opportunity for you to observe how Michael is doing.

(3) Think about your own feelings and what is behind them. Perhaps you feel sneaky, or deceitful, or are simply uncomfortable with not totally telling Michael the truth about his memory loss and possible next steps. You will find yourself needing to make decisions that Michael may well disagree with. In fact, you may need to make them without Michael's knowledge. For most of us, this covert decision-making is counter-intuitive and uncomfortable.

(4) Try to remember that you are acting in Michael's best interest. Feeling guilty is unproductive. If Michael had a sprained ankle or a respiratory infection, or any other purely physical ailment, you would not hesitate to seek treatment for him, and to reassure him that you are on the case. Dealing with Michael's dementia is very different, because he is most likely not aware of his diagnosis, and you will not help him by trying to explain it.

MOVING WITH THE TARGET

Because dementia is a progressive disease, Robin's functioning today may be slightly or dramatically different tomorrow. How can you know if the steps you are contemplating, the decisions you are making for Robin, are what will be best for her? Unfortunately, not by discussing them with her, but by observing, by being honest with yourself, and willing to seek the opinions of experts.

In the short term, you can probably do a great deal to improve Robin's well-being in her home. Robin's physical environment (light, order, hygiene, routine, etc.) can make her much more comfortable and engaged day-to-day. You can easily and inexpensively implement changes at home, but it is usually much more effective to implement them in a clean sweep rather than piecemeal. One easy and immediate safety measure is to get a medical alert system for Robin to wear around her wrist or on a lanyard around her neck. A logical way to present this to Robin, once you have it to show her, is simply to explain, "This button will keep you as safe and independent as possible when you are home by yourself."

Let's consider: For Robin, the environment is the treatment.

Robin's physical safety is paramount, but this is not her only risk factor. Ancillary risks include isolation; lack of mental stimulation; feeling useless, hopeless, or depressed; becoming frightened; or being unable to pinpoint the cause of her anxiety. Because Robin's judgment is impaired, she is vulnerable to elder abuse, which has become increasingly clever and is reaching epidemic proportions.

Robin's nutrition is a great example of something you can easily improve and control, at least for a time. Casually looking in her refrigerator, perhaps by asking if she has any sparkling water, or milk or cream for coffee, is a perfect place to start your research.

Peek in the refrigerator. You yourself cannot look inside Robin's brain to see the progression of her dementia, but you or someone else can easily look inside her refrigerator to see how well she is caring for herself, in terms of nutrition, shopping, and judgment. Even if you are an occasional visitor, you can say you are thirsty and ask if you can see if there is any chilled water in the fridge. Things to scout out:

① Is the refrigerator nearly empty? Any fresh produce? Sources of protein?

② Are there spoiled items and improperly stored leftovers? Any unpleasant odors?

③ Is the pantry stocked with junk food and outdated packages?

Robin may not be a big eater, she may not be much of a cook any more, but she cannot be healthy, or even comfortable, physically or mentally, without adequate nutrition and hydration.

If Robin lives with a partner or with one of her children, then the refrigerator is probably stocked and maintained by that person. In this case, Robin's housemate needs to be aware of what Robin is actually eating or not eating. It is not enough simply to shop and then consider the job done.

You, or someone else, can restock the fridge without making Robin feel that she is not capable of managing her refrigerator. If you go marketing, with or without her, when you put the new groceries away, you can matter-of-factly dispose of the old stuff without making a big deal about it. Depending on Robin's abilities, she may like to help unpack the groceries and organize the fridge, or perhaps not. Either way, she will now have healthy options, which she may not eat. But you will have a baseline inventory—and can tell what she is eating, unless she is throwing it away—so it is a good idea to discreetly rummage in the kitchen trash.

Additional ways to monitor Robin's nutrition include:

① Label items with their expiration dates with a big marker. You can also get a roll of masking tape and write directly on it.

② Take a photo of the freshly stocked fridge so you remember what is in there, and then you have a baseline inventory to see what Robin has eaten.

③ Take a photo of the freezer, if Robin uses frozen foods. Also check the microwave's operability and cleanliness.

④ Remove anything tricky to open from its original packaging and put it in something that Robin can easily maneuver.

BRINGING HELP INTO THE HOME

How are you going to help Robin stay safe? If you determine that she needs help, you actually have "twin tasks." You want to arrange for reliable, compassionate help, and you need to strategize how to make this change without alarming, offending, or frightening Robin. Your options will depend on financial resources and on where Robin lives. If her home is in a city, you will have more professional resources at hand: life care managers, housekeeping services, care agencies, independent caregivers, etc.

It is expensive to hire help, but if you have the financial means, it can be a very good investment. Think of it as buying Robin quality time in her home. If you do not have the means to pay for care, then your best option may be to identify someone, or several someones, in the family or community who can rearrange their schedule(s) to make Robin's home safer for her, as well as to visit with her frequently. You may also be able to find community resources to support you as well.

No matter what you do, you cannot control Robin's disease. You know this on some level, but the way you think, feel, and respond may sometimes be at odds with this basic truth. It is best for any caregiver, including "caring friends" and colleagues, to learn to let go of what you and they cannot control, including not being able to save Robin or make her better. Instead, focus on making her life better in the moment.

If Robin is going to remain in her own home, most likely she will not want to have a care companion per se, because she does not see the need for one. She values her independence and privacy. You will want to present to Robin the idea that what you are proposing will make her life easier and more fun. The short-term objective is for Robin to accept this new person (or people) and become comfortable with their presence. A relationship will develop, and the caregiver's role can expand as Robin's needs evolve and she becomes more comfortable with the care companion.

So, the first step is to get someone who you have vetted in the door. Here are several potentially very effective ideas for introducing this kind of support to Robin:

① Suggest that Robin would enjoy having a personal chef. (The "chef" can consult Robin regarding menus, take her shopping if she is mobile, or make lists per Robin's instructions.) Robin can direct the chef in the kitchen; she can invite the chef to eat with her if she likes; she can set the table for the two of them.

② Suggest that a professional driver, rather than an über or a neighbor, can take Robin on errands and also for scenic drives. (The "driver" will offer to bring groceries and other items into the house and to put them away with Robin, under her direction.)

③ Propose getting Robin an "assistant" to help her once a week with cleaning and laundry. (This person can easily monitor Robin's personal hygiene and overall mobility within her home.)

If you are Robin's adult child, another effective option for introducing a helper into the household is to tell Robin that you are going on a business trip or a vacation, and that you have a good friend who is available to help her in your absence. You can arrange to bring your friend over to meet Robin, and have Robin show your friend around the house, and perhaps the three of you can make a list together of things you normally take care of for Robin. Here is an example of how Stephanie, the daughter of Greta (who is 80 and still lives by herself in her home in West Virginia), approached this challenge.

> Greta was recently diagnosed with vascular dementia and can no longer drive. She feels a tremendous loss of independence because she cannot drive herself places. Some days she is angry at Stephanie about this, blaming her for butting in. Other days, she forgets she can no longer drive, gets ready to go out on errands, and then becomes frustrated when she cannot find her car keys. Greta has called Stephanie, who lives and works in Manhattan, several times in tears.

> For now, Greta would like to stay in her own home but reluctantly agrees to have some help during the day for grocery shopping and errands. Stephanie pitches the idea of the care companion by saying "Mom, it'll be like having your own personal chauffeur. I remember when I was learning to drive, you used to pretend that I was the chauffeur, and you would tell me where you'd like to go. Now, you can tell your new assistant where you want to go. I wish I had one!" Stephanie plans to call a home care agency and specify that she is looking for a combination companion-driver for her mother. She makes notes for herself for the call, including that her ideal candidate will be someone who has a nice car and knows the area extremely well.

Robin's impaired sense of time can make it easier to schedule a care companion several times a week, as Robin may well not remember that the once-a-week helper was over the day before yesterday. If Robin does in fact remember, a skilled caregiver will be comfortable explaining her presence by saying she had a cancellation in her schedule and thought she would drop by to see if Robin needed anything, or even if she would like to go out for coffee or a walk.

Similarly, a brief drop-in, either from a care companion or from you, can seem like a complete visit. On a visit of any length, it is essential to engage with Robin rather than wandering around checking on things. There is no need to point out that your visit was short. But it is worth saying that you enjoyed your visit and look forward to seeing Robin again soon.

If Robin has friends and family close at hand, some of them may be willing to help and to monitor her well-being. However, this needs to be a commitment, not a favor. Someone who is not comfortable chatting with Robin because of her dementia is not going to enjoy being with her, and will not really give her the attention and social interaction she deserves.

Caregiving changes the entire family, not just the person being cared for. The caregiving path will zig and zag unexpectedly as Robin's needs continue to change. Some family members may simply not understand how much help Robin needs, because her level of functioning may vary dramatically from day to day. On Monday, Robin may be her usual self but on Thursday, she seems confused and more forgetful. Actually, such fluctuations can occur from hour to hour. Almost anything, actual or imagined, can set Robin off. (Let's not overlook our favorite culprit, the stealthy urinary tract infection.) Appearances can be deceptive. This unpredictability translates to more guilt and doubt for many family caregivers.

COMMUNICATING YOUR EXPECTATIONS TO CAREGIVERS

The more aware you are of what Robin needs, and the more specific you can be for a caregiver, the better the outcome you can achieve. Write down your expectations and task descriptions to review with a caregiver, ideally in person, to make sure he or she understands them. A checklist can include specific instructions. Finding someone to help Robin is not at all like hiring a gardener or a plumber. Robin's needs are personal and unique to her.

All agencies, caregivers, and other providers have their own lists of what categories of service they provide, but one size truly does not fit all. Your opportunity to clarify what Robin needs and what you expect, is at the very beginning, even before you sign a contract or agreement, and definitely before a caregiver is assigned. It is not fair to Robin to hide any of her limitations from the person or people you are engaging to help her. The last thing you want is for a caregiver to ignore Robin's needs, either because of unawareness or lack of physical strength or simply a not-my-job attitude. Robin cannot advocate for herself, and she may well not remember her own limitations, so may not think to ask for help.

Many grown children or partners put their trust and their financial resources in an agency or individual caregiver without putting in place an ongoing way to monitor the quality, effectiveness, and consistency of care. It is risky to abdicate oversight. You have to make sure caregivers are doing their job. The most effective caregivers have—more important than their organizational skills, more than their overriding tidiness—a big heart and a sense of humor in the moment.

Dr. Jane's oversight practice includes having caregivers send her, via text or email, notes on the day: what Robin did, how she seemed, and what domestic tasks the caregiver took care of. If you do not have a Dr. Jane, you are totally entitled to have the caregiver send you, either directly or via the agency, this sort of regular update.

ORGANIZING ROBIN'S DAY

You or a care companion can easily add a sense of purpose to Robin's day. Many people with dementia do well with having a routine. A predictable schedule for the day does not preclude the possibility of a pleasant surprise or spontaneous activity, but it does provide a structure that makes getting up, getting dressed, and having breakfast seem like the logical first steps in the productive day ahead. Feeling productive is remarkably therapeutic for combatting depression and for lowering anxiety. Even if Robin's morning is solitary, "getting going" is engaging, making Robin feel that she is ready to meet the day.

Using a paper-and-pencil calendaring system can help Robin in several ways. First, it alleviates her anxiety that she might have missed something she cannot remember. Second, it allows her to see upcoming engagements and, therefore, to look forward to them. Because of her memory limitations, she can actually experience this pleasure of anticipation over and over again. And, last but not least, it allows her to feel in control of her own schedule—and that feeling of control is quite empowering. You can review Robin's calendar in a conversational way, and just doing this makes her feel engaged. (There is no benefit to using a tone that conveys, "You are so forgetful that we have to write everything down.") If you are not able to review the schedule in person with Robin, technology makes it easy for you to have a duplicate to refer to, and you can remind Robin that you have a copy of her schedule.

FEAR OF BATHING: WHAT'S BEHIND IT?

Many caregivers categorize bathing someone as their most daunting responsibility. It is not rare for a person with dementia to stop using the shower or bathtub for its intended purpose and start using it as a storage space.

Obviously, if the shower or tub is full of boxes or worse, Robin is not bathing. She may or may not be aware of this, and may profess surprise if you point out that she cannot use her shower or tub. Contradicting her will not be effective, nor will using a bossy tone. Robin may actually have become afraid of showering, for one of several reasons:

① Confusion — Showering is a somewhat complex task, one you do not even think about, but it requires not only a sequence of steps, but also adjustment for temperature. If Robin gets confused and scalds herself or steps into a cold shower, she will remember this, but will not necessarily be able to figure out what she has done to cause it. She will think the shower is to blame.

② Chill — She doesn't like being cold after she undresses for her shower, and/or being cold when she gets out.

③ Pain — She may have chronic pain (in her hip, shoulder, or elsewhere), and somehow associates this with having to undress, shower, and get dressed again.

④ Embarrassment—If Robin needs help in the shower, she may dislike the presence of another person while she is undressed.

It is not uncommon for people with dementia to actually become frightened of water, particularly on their faces. It is possible to work around this without bossing or treating Robin like a baby. One respectful, non-threatening approach is to suggest that Robin might enjoy soaking her feet, which she can do while seated and clothed. It is then possible to work your way up and ask Robin if she would like you to add more water, so she can soak her ankles and even her calves. You or a caregiver can pretend that the luxurious footbath is Robin's usual routine.

You can also find plausible "social reasons" to suggest a footbath or shower, such as telling Robin that so-and-so is coming to visit in an hour, so she'll want to freshen up for her guest. Or you might remind her that she'll be going out later in the day and will want to clean up so she'll be ready.

Shower safety should be your first priority. If Robin's shower or tub is in working order, is soap within easy and secure reach? (If the soap is cracked, this is a likely indicator that it hasn't been used in a while.) What about grab bars? These are essential for minimizing her risk of falling. A shower chair is an additional safety measure, reducing Robin's need to support herself and increasing her opportunity to enjoy the warm water.

You actually have twin objectives: to have Robin bathe and to help her enjoy the experience. You need to respect her personal preferences, which may not be the same as yours. Additionally, her preferences may have changed from those you remember. She may have developed a new physical routine and even a new mental routine, in terms of the times of day when she is higher functioning, more alert, more sleepy, etc.

Now it is time to consider who is going to help Robin shower. This will depend on her living situation. If she lives alone, a caregiver who is not a family member probably has more experience and confidence doing this than an adult child. And, frankly, Robin may be more comfortable with a "shower lady" than with one of her children. If Robin lives with her partner or grown child(ren), an outside caregiver is still a good option, if financially feasible. Again, everyone's dementia is different, and showering can be a chronic source of agitation for some people.

Making bathing comforting and safe

Showering is essential for hygiene, but it is also a wonderful opportunity for sensory enjoyment. Robin may be delighted by the addition of simple amenities to her showering experience. These are also great to try even if Robin is only having a footbath, and she may find them so pleasurable that you can propose washing her back for her if she would like to sit in the shower. Possible enticements include:

① Adding oil or bubble bath to a footbath will make it smell nice and feel special. You can easily carry on a conversation with Robin while she enjoys the interlude.

② Putting Robin's towel in the dryer for a few minutes while she is showering will provide her with a very cozy towel in which to be wrapped. Warming her robe is also a treat.

(3) Playing music, especially oldies or others of Robin's favorites, is almost always something Robin will enjoy. As part of Robin's bathing ritual, music becomes auditory pampering.

(4) Creating mood lighting adds to the relaxing aspect. An aromatic candle can provide a total sensory experience for Robin (without posing any risk, as you or a caregiver will not leave Robin alone for an instant while she is bathing).

> **DR. JANE SAYS**
>
> Human touch and personal attention, even from a non-loved one, can be therapeutic.

Touches like these can make showering seem luxurious, and make Robin feel special rather than threatened or bossed.

CHANGE: THE PROVERBIAL ELEPHANT IN THE ROOM

Most plans we make in life are for improving a situation, whether it is saving money, losing weight, or looking for a new home or job. In Robin's case, her dementia will not be improving—rather, it is the quality of her life that you are trying to improve. Though this level of quality may make you feel uncomfortable, sad, or frustrated, your goal is to keep Robin as comfortable, engaged, and safe as possible, without making her feel that her quality of life has diminished.

You may have been tiptoeing around the prospect of making changes to Robin's living situation. You may even have felt afraid to broach the subject, or you may even have decided that a wait-and-see approach will be less stressful for you and for Robin. However, if you do not make a realistic, pro-active plan, dementia will, seemingly overnight, dramatically reduce your options or even precipitate a crisis.

As we have said before, caring for someone with dementia is a moving and unpredictable target. A short-term plan is exactly that. Making a long-term plan before you need it is incredibly prudent. If you do not know what your options are, you will be caught off guard and unable to make the best decisions. The support groups organized by local Alzheimer's Association chapters are an excellent free resource, providing a non-threatening setting for discussing Robin's limitations and your concerns, and for gaining tips and insights from others in circumstances similar to yours. Some families are financially able to consult with a life care manager or gerontologist, to assess Robin's overall functioning and to recommend next steps to keep Robin safe and engaged. (In Chapter 4, *Getting Help & Being Helpful*, we describe how support groups work.)

ON THE MOVE: PLANNING FOR ROBIN'S FUTURE

When is the right time to either bring outside caregivers into Robin's home or to move her to an assisted living or memory care community? This is a complex question, and the answer is extremely personal. Four main factors may play into your decision:

① Finances, including the value of Robin's home

② Robin's disease progression, including behavior issues

③ Where Robin lives and where her family lives

④ The emotional intangibles, including family dynamics

Some family members feel guilty when they weigh the pros and cons of moving Robin from her home. It is normal to project our own feelings, but Robin's needs are different than ours. Do not let guilt immobilize or blind you to what can be best for Robin. One approach does not fit all. Every Robin is different, because everybody's brain is different. It can be tricky to determine when the balance of benefit (Robin's independence!) and risk reaches a tipping point.

Objectively speaking, if Robin's dementia has progressed so that she is no longer able to care for herself (including dressing, bathing, eating, and what we call "acts of connecting": using the telephone, operating the remote, differentiating between the doorbell and the microwave timer), then she poses a safety risk to herself. Some

Robins may be able to do all of these things, but have lost the ability to find their way from the garden back into the house, or their judgment may be so impaired that they are likely to offer to help anyone who asks, particularly for money. These red flags indicate that it is high time to take action to protect Robin. She cannot be the best judge of what would be best for her. And this is a huge sticking point in many families. How you express upcoming changes to Robin and implement them will have a big impact on how she adjusts.

The physical signs of transition that many of us welcome when we are making changes tend to be confusing or upsetting for people with dementia. Stacks of clothes to be donated, overflowing recycling, plastic bags of trash—all of which may symbolize to you spring cleaning—may make Robin anxious, as if the domestic rug were being pulled out from under her. If you will be moving a caregiver into Robin's spare room or moving Robin out of her home, whether to live with another family member or in a memory care community, the key is to accomplish this with as little stress and sense of change as possible for Robin.

If you can accept whatever changes you are going to make as positive, as steps to make Robin safer and more engaged, you will have an easier time conveying this, directly and indirectly, to Robin. You may find telling the "*kind* kind of lie" extremely helpful. If your resources permit, contacting a life care manager or gerontologist may be a wise investment, to help you orchestrate the upcoming changes. Regardless, it is important for you not to feel that you have failed in your objective.

Even though you will not beat Robin's dementia, you can enrich her moment-living life and still find new ways to connect with her. For Robin, as for all of us, feeling acknowledged and valued (rather than feeling ignored or alone), can make a world of difference.

Acknowledgments

We are grateful to many people for their help, wisdom, and encouragement in this endeavor. We would like to express our thanks particularly to our first readers for their sharp eyes and keen ears: Ann Flower, Donna Galletti, Dr. David Gehret, Nan Heflin LMFT, Jen Jerde, Dr. Rebecca Shoda-Meyer, Leslie Thomsen, Cynthia Tusan, and Ann Worthington.

We are grateful as well to neurologist William Shankle, who wrote the insightful foreword. The clinic in Orange County that bears his name combines his voice of experience with his compassionate attention to "the devilish details" of dementia care—and an outlook of optimism for the future of Alzehimer's interventions.

Ginna and David Gordon of Lucky Valley Press stewarded us through every step of the independent publishing process, masterfully guiding us to the starting gate.

Citations

The citations support statistics and trends mentioned early in *I hear you*. For the most part, they reference research studies cited by the National Institutes of Health (NIH), either under the auspices of the National Center for Biotechnology Information (NCBI) or the National Institute of Neurological Disorders and Stroke (NINDS).

CHAPTER 1
CLARIFYING THREE OF THE FOUR D-WORDS

Page 5

1 Park, Kyoung S., et al. "The effect of physical activity on cognition relative to APOE genotype (PAAD-2): study protocol for a phase II randomized control trial." *BMC Neurology* 20. 231 (2020). *ProQuest.*

2 Prasad, K. "AGE–RAGE stress: a changing landscape in pathology and treatment of Alzheimer's disease." *Molecular and Cellular Biochemistry* 459 (2019): 95–112. *ProQuest.*

Page 6

3 Padmadas, N., Panda, P.K., and Durairaj, S. "Binding Patterns Associated Aß-HSP60 p. 458 Conjugate to HLA-DR-DRB Allele of Human in Alzheimer's Disease: An In Silico Approach." *Interdisciplinary Sciences Computational Life Sciences* 10 (2018): 93–104. *ProQuest.*

4 Moss, Donald E. "Improving Anti-Neurodegenerative Benefits of Acetylcholinesterase Inhibitors in Alzheimer's Disease: Are Irreversible Inhibitors the Future?" *International Journal of Molecular Sciences* 21.10 (2020): 3438. *ProQuest.*

[5] Beam, Christopher R. et al. "Differences Between Women and Men in Incidence Rates of Dementia and Alzheimer's Disease." *Journal of Alzheimer's Disease* 64. 4 (2018): 1077–1083. *NCBI Resources.*

[6] Plassman, B.L. et al. "Prevalence of dementia in the United States: The Aging, Demographics, and Memory Study." *Neuroepidemiology* 29. 1–2 (2007): 125–32. *Alzheimer's Association.*

Page 7

[7] Nazarian, A., Yashin, A., and Kulminski, A. "Genome-wide analysis of genetic predisposition to Alzheimer's disease and related sex disparities." *Alzheimer's Research & Therapy* 11. 5 (2019). *Springer.*

[8] Perkovic, Matea N., and Pivac, Nela. "Genetic Markers of Alzheimer's Disease." *Frontiers in Psychiatry* (2019): 27–52. *PubMed.*

[9] Zanetti, O., Solerte, SB., and Cantoni, F. "Life expectancy in Alzheimer's disease (AD)." *Archives of Gerontology and Geriatrics* 49.1 (2009): 237–243. PubMed. Web. 12 Aug. 2020.

Page 9

[10] Lin, Frank R., and Albert, Marilyn. "Hearing Loss and Dementia—Who's Listening?" *Aging & Mental Health.* 2014 Aug; 18(6): 671–673. NCBI.

Page 10

[11] Chare, L. et al. "New criteria for frontotemporal dementia syndromes: clinical and pathological diagnostic implications." *Journal of Neurology, Neurosurgery & Psychiatry* 85. 8 (2014): 866–871. *BMJ Journals.*

[12] Finger, Elizabeth C. "Frontotemporal Dementias." *Continuum: American Academy of Neurology* 22. 2 (2016): 464–489. NCBI.

[13] NIH. "Frontotemporal Disorders: Hope Through Research." NINDS 14–6361 (2014).

[14] Bott, N. et al. "Frontotemporal dementia: diagnosis, deficits, and management." *Neurodegenerative Disease Management*. 4.6 (2014): 439–454. NCBI.

CHAPTER 2
ACKNOWLEDGING EARLY-ONSET DEMENTIA

Page 17

[15] Draper, B. and Withall, A. "Young Onset Dementia." *Internal Medicine Journal* 47. 7 (2016). Wiley.

Resources

IF YOU SEEK HELP VIA PHONE OR IN PERSON, consider that you learn more when you listen than when you talk. A perceptive helpline staffer, social worker, or life care manager will ask you key questions, but you can also ask questions. Simply going into great detail about what you need is not enough to get you the answers or help you're looking for.

UNITED STATES

AGING LIFE CARE ASSOCIATION   aginglifecare.org

The central feature of this site is a listing of members, whose services you can arrange for directly (rather than through the Association). Life care managers evaluate the needs of people with various physical limitations and/or mental impairments, and then develop a plan and coordinate care. You may decide that a single consultation provides enough guidance, or you may find that working with a life care manager on an on-going basis can be very helpful. The site includes extensive listings of practitioners, and thus can be a helpful starting point.

AGING WITH DIGNITY   agingwithdignity.org

A national non-profit organization based in Florida, with the primary focus of improving end-of-life care by making medical decisions in advance of a serious or chronic illness. One of Aging With Dignity's programs is Five Wishes, an extensive form that allows you to express your wishes. Copies are modestly priced, and can be filled out online or by hand (in over two dozen languages).

ALZHEIMER'S ASSOCIATION   alz.org

The national umbrella organization for regional chapters in every state. The Alzheimer's Association is the largest non-profit funder of Alzheimer's disease research in the United States. At alz.org, you can find a complete listing of regional chapters with direct links to their respective sites. The Association sponsors support groups, maintains a 24/7 help line (1.800.272.3900), presents educational programs, and provides updates on current research and clinical trials. The Association's major fundraising event is the Walk to End Alzheimer's.

The alz.org/blog is a forum where both caregivers and people with Alzheimer's can share their stories and concerns, and where suggestions are offered in response. The blog is a public forum, open to anyone anywhere.

ALZHEIMER'S ORANGE COUNTY (ALZOC)   alzoc.org

This stand-alone non-profit is located on Dr. Jane Mahakian's home court. Alzheimer's Orange County provides support to Orange County families and individuals through brain health and dementia education, care consultations, community resource connections, adult day health services, residential, memory care services, and more.

ASSOCIATION FOR FRONTOTEMPORAL
DEGENERATION (AFTD)   theaftd.org

AFTD is a non profit organization dedicated to improving the life of people affected by FTD. It was founded in 2002 and has grown to be an international expert on FTD and young-onset dementia. They provide many resources for caregivers and people diagnosed with FTD, including a national helpline, recommended reading list, and grants.

FAMILY CAREGIVER ALLIANCE (FCA)   caregiver.org

Started about 40 years ago, FCA is a non-profit organization whose mission is to improve the quality of life for family caregivers and people who receive their care. Their caregiver education program includes webinars, videos, articles, and handy fact sheets. FCA annually administers a series of awards for other nonprofits, universities, or government agencies developing novel approaches to support people with dementia and their caregivers.

HOSPICE FOUNDATION OF AMERICA (HFA)

hospicefoundation.org

Hospice Foundation of America educates the public and health care professionals about death, dying and grief. HFA brings together the nation's leading experts to contribute to the content of HFA's books, web-based tutorials and programs, and videos. Hospice Foundation of America also funds research about hospice care, supports specific hospice and/or grief initiatives.

NATIONAL ALLIANCE FOR CAREGIVING (NAC)   caregiving.org

Founded in 1996 by Gail Gibson Hunt, the organization has become a powerful advocate for caregivers in the public policy arena. The year following its founding, NAC published in partnership with AARP, "Caregiving in the U.S," the first research study of its kind. The 2020 edition, still in partnership with AARP, is currently available as a free download on the NAC site.

The general caregiving area of the site includes an extensive, detailed listing of NAC's partner organizations and their various specialties. "Alzheimer's & Dementia Caregiving" has its own helpful, specific section.

NATIONAL INSTITUTE ON AGING (NIA)   nia.nih.gov

The NIA's mission is to improve the health and well-being of older Americans through research. It is a division of the U.S. National Institutes of Health (NIH), located in Bethesda, Maryland. (The NIA itself is headquartered nearby in Baltimore.) The website is both deep and broad. You can find science-based health and wellness information, detailed articles written in plain language for caregivers, and up-to-the-minute developments in research initiatives and clinical trials.

PARKINSON'S FOUNDATION   parkinson.org

The mission of this national organization is to make life better for people with Parkinson's disease by improving care and advancing research toward a cure. The site states that 70 percent of people with Parkinson's will develop dementia as their disease progresses. However, Parkinson's Disease Dementia is not a form of Alzheimer's.

WOMEN'S ALZHEIMER'S MOVEMENT

thewomensalzheimersmovement.org

Founded by Maria Shriver in 2010, WAM is dedicated to finding an answer to a perplexing medical conundrum: Why are two of every three people who develop Alzheimer's women? Secondarily, WAM asks: Why are women of color at even higher risk? The organization fundraises with unwavering focus to support women-based research and initiatives at leading institutions. The website includes "Tips & Tools for Brain Health" as well as personal stories and advice for caregivers. WAM's occasional online programs, typically exactly one hour, present several experts and/or patients living proactively with dementia. Maria Shriver, a trained journalist, is an excellent listener and question-asker.

INTERNATIONAL

ALZHEIMER'S CARE ARMENIA (ACA)   alzheimerscarearmenia.org

ACA is a California-based non-profit founded by Dr. Jane Mahakian in 2017, with the mission of developing sustainable programs and services for people with Alzheimer's disease and other dementias in Armenia. In 2018, ACA coordinated the first-ever Alzheimer's disease conference for family caregivers in Armenia. More recently, ACA developed, in conjunction with the Armenia Ministry of Health and Mission Armenia, a national Alzheimer's disease caregiver helpline.

ALZHEIMER'S DISEASE INTERNATIONAL (ADI)   alz.co.uk

ADI is the umbrella organization for over 100 Alzheimer's associations around the globe. ADI works to raise global awareness about Alzheimer's disease and other dementias. Member organizations offer support to people with dementia and those who care for them. ADI's advocacy includes campaigning for policy change from governments and the World Health Organization, as well as strengthening associations around the globe. In the spring of 2020, early in the pandemic, ADI mobilized quickly to serve as a "virtual global information resource" for families, healthcare professionals, and care communities struggling to re-think how to care for people living with dementia.

ALZHEIMER SOCIETY OF CANADA   alzheimer.ca

This is the umbrella organization for chapters in the various provinces, which in turn provide support to offices in major cities. Even if you don't live in Canada, you can access a great deal of practical information as well as personal stories. A separate site (findingyourwayontario.ca) provides tips for preventing someone with dementia from wandering off, and for minimizing risks if it happens. Major content is available in multiple languages, from Arabic to Urdu, including the "A Walk With Dementia" video. Additional downloadable resources are available in English.

Other Books You
Might Find Helpful

ANOTHER COUNTRY:
NAVIGATING THE EMOTIONAL TERRAIN OF OUR ELDERS
Mary Pipher, PhD

The author is a psychologist; originally published in 2000, this book was a *New York Times* bestseller. The "other country" doesn't refer to dementia specifically, but to old age in general. Dr. Pipher offers helpful insights into the big differences between Baby Boomers' and their parents' approach to discussing personal issues and asking for help. This broader perspective can be extremely helpful for grown children, or even contemporaries, in communicating respectfully and realistically with an older person living with dementia.

CREATING MOMENTS OF JOY ALONG THE ALZHEIMER'S
JOURNEY: A GUIDE FOR FAMILIES AND CAREGIVERS
Jolene Brackey

Originally published in 2009, this friendly and upbeat book has been revised and expanded for its fifth edition. The author, Jolene Brackey, doesn't seem to have any specific education in the field that we have found—but the book has earned thousands of positive reviews from readers. It is primarily a succession of short vignettes that are easy to understand, though the author does not go into much depth. Her instincts are good, but she doesn't provide much specific guidance for people whose instincts are not.

ELDERHOOD: REDEFINING AGING, TRANSFORMING MEDICINE, REIMAGINING LIFE
Louise Aronson, MD

Dr. Aronson is a geriatrician, educator, and professor of medicine at the University of California, San Francisco. Her book's focus is on old age and how our society, medically and culturally, regards and treats people in their elderhood. She is engaging and compassionate, and many of the anecdotes are applicable to the care of people with dementia. Dr. Aronson also reflects on the rigors of medical training and on her personal experiences with ageism.

LEARNING TO SPEAK ALZHEIMER'S: A GROUNDBREAKING APPROACH FOR EVERYONE DEALING WITH THE DISEASE (2003)
Joanne Koenig Coste

The author's husband developed early-onset Alzheimer's when he was only 44—and she was pregnant with their fourth child. She cared for her husband at home until his death four years later. The book's section on communicating is strong, and the author weaves excellent examples throughout the book. Although her primary first-hand experience was with one case of early-onset Alzheimer's, she has since become an advocate for "habilitation" (her word) and a consultant to memory-care facilities.

STILL ALICE (2007)
Lisa Genova

This fictional story of early-onset Alzheimer's is told from the perspective of a Harvard professor in her 40s. The book was made into a popular movie produced by Maria Shriver (2014). Alice, in response to having her "career rug" pulled out from under her, finds herself feeling incredibly isolated. She is able to advocate for the logic and benefit of having a support group for patients. Alice and three other people living with early-onset dementia form a little group, and they become major supports for one another.

Near the end of the book, Alice is invited to give the opening plenary presentation for the annual Dementia Care Conference of the Alzheimer's Association. Her entire talk, which she reads without lifting her eyes from her typed speech, lest she lose her place, is included, and it is a brilliant and moving summary of what it is like to find that you have become marginalized, disregarded, and pitied—and that many people don't really listen when you talk.

CPSIA information can be obtained
at www.ICGtesting.com
Printed in the USA
BVHW091046240221
600902BV00003B/479